Essential Texts

Anthology

COMPILED BY

Brian Moses

Contents

stories by significant children's writers

~ Toothie and Cat   4
by Gene Kemp

~ Licked   8
by Paul Jennings

playscripts

~ Telling Tales   12
by Trevor Harvey

~ Abducted by Aliens   16
by Ian Souter

poetry by significant children's writers

~ My Mother Saw a Dancing Bear   18
by Charles Causley

~ What has Happened to Lulu?   19
by Charles Causley

novel by significant children's writer

~ Friend or Foe   20
by Michael Morpurgo

concrete poetry

~ Up in the Attic   26
by Wes Magee

~ The Concrete Poem   28
by Noel Petty

~ The Platform Arriving ...   29
by Gina Douthwaite

myths, legends and fables from a range of cultures

~ In the Beginning and Pandora's Box   30
retold by Geraldine McCaughrean

~ How Night Came to the World   34
retold by Sean Taylor

~ The Fox and the Crane   38
retold by Sean Taylor

The Tortoise and the Baboon   39
retold by Sean Taylor

	Bedd Gelert *retold by Stephen Corrin*	40
longer classic poetry	Beth Gêlert *by William Robert Spencer*	42
	The Highwayman *by Alfred Noyes*	44
	A Smuggler's Song *by Rudyard Kipling*	48
traditional stories	Beauty and the Beast *retold by Dennis Hamley*	50
	Billy Beast *by Laurence Anholt*	52
stories from a variety of cultures and traditions	Grandpa Chatterji *by Jamila Gavin*	56
	The Mouth-organ Boys *by James Berry*	62
poetry from a variety of cultures and traditions	The Pow-wow Drum *by David Campbell*	68
	The Snake Song *by John Mbiti*	70
	Chicken Dinner *by Valerie Bloom*	71
novel from a different culture and tradition	No Gun for Asmir *by Christobel Mattingly*	72
older literature	Black Beauty *by Anna Sewell*	76
performance poetry	Unwillingly to School *by Gregory Harrison*	78
	Conversation Piece *by Gareth Owen*	79

Toothie and Cat

GENE KEMP

High on the hills above the city was a cave, well hidden away among the trees and the rocks and the bracken. And in that cave lived an old tramp with a gingery, greyish beard hanging to his waist, a greasy hat on his head, string tied just below the knees of his trousers, and one tooth that stuck out over his beard. Because of this he was known as Toothie, and he couldn't remember very much at all, for his brain was as foggy as a November night. He was never bright even in his prime and he hadn't improved with the

10 years. Nobody had ever cared for him much ever since his mother dumped him, wrapped in an old blanket, outside a police station, and then made off as fast as she could. Toothie tried to keep away from police stations ever after.

Below the hills in the city lived Cat. Cat the Black and the Bad, a streak of a cat with claws as sharp as daggers and a heart as black as his tatty fur. No one loved Cat. Once he was dropped in a river and left to drown. But you don't drown animals like Cat that easily. He got out, and survived, by hatred, mostly. He hated people and children and bright

20 lights and kindness. He loved fighting and stealing, roof-tops and alleys, and, most of all, dustbins. He relied on them when the birds grew careful, or too many kitchen doors were shut. In the daytime he thieved and slept on walls in patches of sunlight. At night he rampaged across roof-tops, wailing and caterwauling. So he lived for some years, till one morning he dropped from a roof-top a bit carelessly, and a car speeding through the dawn grazed his leg. Snarling and swearing, he limped to the side of the road, where Toothie, who had also been raiding dustbins,

30 found him. He was pleased, for he'd found a very meaty chicken carcase.

He walked all round Cat, who spat at him. Then he popped a bit of chicken into the complaining mouth, and Cat stopped spitting, and ate instead. Toothie popped him in his old bag, and went back to the cave, where he made some chicken soup and tied a big leaf round the injured leg. After a time Cat stopped spitting at him, for he'd grown to like Toothie's smell. His leg healed.

Cat did not return to the city. It was summer. He hunted and Toothie cooked: stews and soups in his iron pot, other tasty dishes baked in mud packed at the base of the fire. Long warm days passed by in the green wood and the dark cave. Sometimes Toothie would sing and Cat purr, both rusty noises. That autumn was beautiful, warm and golden, with more nuts than had been seen for years. Toothie and Cat were well fed and content.

Until the night the October wind arrived, blowing cold, stripping the leaves off the trees, and it brought with it the sound of cats singing in the city below. Cat stirred in his sleep and woke up. He left Toothie's warmth to sit in the mouth of the cave, listening. Yes, there, again, came the yowling of cats. Cat shivered. He looked once at the old man, asleep, and slipped out into the night.

A fortnight later he came back, hungry, limping, wet and exhausted, longing for Toothie's warm fire, Toothie's food, Toothie's smelly company. But the cave was empty. The iron pot hung forlornly by the burnt-out fire. Toothie had gone.

Cat sat and washed himself, which is what cats do when they don't know what to do next. Then he searched through the woods, crying his strange, wild call. There was no Toothie. Cat slew an unwary bird who would have done better to have migrated and, still hungry, set off for the city.

Through the streets he ran, sniffing, investigating, fighting, always searching for Toothie's fascinating smell, and one day, a week or so later, he arrived at the City Hospital and knew that his friend was inside.

Now Cat was much cleverer than Toothie, and he knew from the smell of the hospital that that was where people were ill, and his cat brain put illness and chicken together.

70   He'd got to find some chicken.

He tried as many houses as he had paws before he finally crept into a gleaming, shiny bright kitchen, and there on the immaculate tiled surface lay a scrumptious chicken leg on a plate of crisp salad. The salad Cat ignored, he was not a lettuce-eater, but he seized the chicken and was just about to leap through the partially open window when the owner appeared, screamed like a whistling kettle and spent the rest of the day feeling very ill indeed, and telling anyone who could be made to listen how a fiendish monster had

80   appeared like a black demon in her sacred kitchen. Cat kept increasing in size till he reached the dimensions of a mini-tiger.

A while later, the mini-tiger sat outside the hospital door and waited, chicken portion gripped firmly in teeth. Going in at the front door didn't seem like a good idea – it looked too busy and important. Cat had never liked front doors, anyway. Back or side doors were for the likes of him. So he slunk round the corner till he came to a dark staircase that went up and up and on and on. Right at the

90   top were dozens of dustbins. Cat purred through the chicken. He liked those dustbins, homely and friendly, they were.

Beyond them was a door with two little round glass panels. It opened in the middle and swung as someone walked through. And Cat slid in, keeping a very low profile. He ran, chicken in mouth and stomach almost on the floor, through rows of beds, and then into another ward with yet more beds. In the third a little boy lay in bed, bored. He sat up and cried: 'There's a cat. It's got something in its mouth.

100   Good ole puss cat. Come here.'

He wanted Cat a lot, but Cat ran on. But now that he was spotted, pandemonium broke loose.

'Catch that cat!'

6

'Stop him!'

'Get that filthy animal out of here!'

As fast as he could, Cat ran on. Patients shouted as nurses ran to grab him.

But nothing could stop Cat now. Like a rocket swooshing into space, Cat shot down the ward to find Toothie. He
110 dodged trolleys, ran under beds, ran over beds, squeezed between legs, narrowly missed cleaners, tripped up nurses carrying vases of flowers or trays, scattering people right and left to reach the bed with the screens round it where Toothie lay dying.

He'd collapsed with pneumonia a week after Cat had left him and somehow, shivering, coughing, full of pains, he'd crawled to the road, where a bus driver had driven him straight to the hospital despite complaints from some of the passengers. And since then, Toothie had lain in terror of the
120 bright lights, the uniforms, the smells and the sounds, all too much for his mazed mind. He wanted to die.

Sister's voice rang out loud and clear.

'Stop that beast! It's got germs!'

Hands grabbed at Cat, missing narrowly. He shot through the screens and the doctor and nurses beside Toothie and up on to the bed. There on the whiter than white, brighter than bright, snowy, frosty, bleached, purified, disinfected, sterilised, decontaminated pillow Cat laid the dusty, greasy, tooth-marked chicken leg, just beside
130 Toothie's head.

Shouts were all about him.

But Toothie's eyes opened and he saw Cat. A triumphant burst of purring sounded through the ward. Come what might, Cat had arrived.
He'd found Toothie.

Illustrated by Peter Sutton

Licked

Paul Jennings

1 Tomorrow when Dad calms down I'll own up. Tell him the truth. He might laugh. He might cry. He might strangle me. But I have to put him out of his misery.

I like my dad. He takes me fishing. He gives me arm wrestles in front of the fire on cold nights. He plays Scrabble instead of watching the news. He tries practical jokes on me. And he keeps his promises. Always.

But he has two faults. Bad faults. One is to do with flies. He can't stand them. If there's a fly in the room he has to
10   kill it. He won't use fly spray because of the ozone layer so he chases them with a fly swat. He races around the house swiping and swatting like a mad thing. He won't stop until the fly is flat. Squashed. Squished – sometimes still squirming on the end of the fly swat.

He's a dead-eye shot. He hardly ever misses. When his old fly swat was almost worn out I bought him a nice new yellow one for his birthday. It wasn't yellow for long. It soon had bits of fly smeared all over it.

It's funny the different colours that squashed flies have
20   inside them. Mostly it is black or brown. But often there are streaks of runny red stuff and sometimes bits of blue. The wings flash like diamonds if you hold them up to the light. But mostly the wings fall off unless they are stuck to the swat with a bit of squashed innards.

2 Chasing flies is Dad's first fault. His second one is table manners. He is mad about manners.

And it is always my manners that are the matter.
'Andrew,' he says. 'Don't put your elbows on the table.'
'Don't talk with your mouth full.'
30   'Don't lick your fingers.'
'Don't dunk your biscuit in the coffee.'

This is the way he goes on every meal time. He has a thing about flies and a thing about manners.

Anyway, to get back to the story. One day Dad is peeling the potatoes for tea. I am looking for my fifty cents that rolled under the table about a week ago. Mum is cutting up the cabbage and talking to Dad. They do not know that I am there. It is a very important meal because Dad's boss, Mr Spinks, is coming for tea. Dad never stops going on 40 about my manners when someone comes for tea.

'You should stop picking on Andrew at tea time,' says Mum.

'I don't,' says Dad.

'Yes you do,' says Mum. 'It's always "don't do this, don't do that." You'll give the boy a complex.'

I have never heard of a complex before but I guess that it is something awful like pimples.

'Tonight,' says Mum. 'I want you to go for the whole meal without telling Andrew off once.'

50 'Easy,' says Dad.

'Try hard,' says Mum. 'Promise me that you won't get cross with him.'

Dad looks at her for a long time. 'Okay,' he says. 'It's a deal. I won't say one thing about his manners. But you're not allowed to either. What's good for me is good for you.'

'Shake,' says Mum. They shake hands and laugh.

I find the fifty cents and sneak out. I take a walk down the street to spend it before tea. Dad has promised not to tell me off at tea time. I think about how I can make him 60 crack. It should be easy. I will slurp my soup. He hates that. He will tell me off. He might even yell. I just know that he can't go for the whole meal without going crook. 'This is going to be fun,' I say to myself.

3 That night Mum sets the table with the new tablecloth. And the best knives and forks. And the plates that I am not allowed to touch. She puts out serviettes in little rings. All of this means that it is an important meal. We don't usually use serviettes.

Mr Spinks comes in his best suit. He wears gold glasses and
he frowns a lot. I can tell that he doesn't like children. You can
always tell when adults don't like kids. They smile at you with
their lips but not with their eyes.

Anyway, we sit down to tea. I put my secret weapon on the
floor under the table. I'm sure that I can make Dad crack
without using it. But it is there if all else fails.

The first course is soup and bread rolls. I make loud
slurping noises with the soup. No one says anything about it. I
make the slurping noises longer and louder. They go on and
on and on. It sounds like someone has pulled the plug out of
the bath. Dad clears his throat but doesn't say anything.

I try something different. I dip my bread in the soup and
make it soggy. Then I hold it high above my head and drop it
down into my mouth. I catch it with a loud slopping noise. I
try again with an even bigger bit. This time I miss my mouth
and the bit of soupy bread hits me in the eye.

Nothing is said. Dad looks at me. Mum looks at me. Mr
Spinks tries not to look at me. They are talking about how Dad
might get a promotion at work. They are pretending that I am
not revolting.

The next course is chicken. Dad will crack over the chicken.
He'll say something. He hates me picking up the bones.

The chicken is served. 'I've got the chicken's bottom,' I say
in a loud voice.

Dad glares at me but he doesn't answer. I pick up the
chicken and start stuffing it into my mouth with my fingers. I
grab a roast potato and break it in half. I dip my fingers into
the margarine and put some on the potato. It runs all over the
place.

I have never seen anyone look as mad as the way Dad looks
at me. He glares. He stares. He clears his throat. But still he
doesn't crack. What a man. Nothing can make him break his
promise.

I snap a chicken bone in half and suck out the middle. It is
hollow and I can see right through it. I suck and slurp and

swallow. Dad is going red in the face. Little veins are standing out on his nose. But still he does not crack.

The last course is baked apple and custard. I will get him with that. Mr Spinks has stopped talking about Dad's promotion. He is discussing something about discipline. About setting limits. About insisting on standards. Something like that. I put the hollow bone into the custard and use it like a straw. I suck the custard up the hollow chicken bone.

Dad clears his throat. He is very red in the face. 'Andrew,' he says.

He is going to crack. I have won.

'Yes,' I say through a mouth full of custard.

'Nothing,' he mumbles.

Dad is terrific. He is under enormous pressure but still he keeps his cool. There is only one thing left to do. I take out my secret weapon.

4 I place the yellow fly swat on the table next to my knife. Everyone looks at it lying there on the white tablecloth. They stare and stare and stare. But nothing is said.

I pick up the fly swat and start to lick it. I lick it like an ice cream. A bit of chewy, brown goo comes off on my tongue. I swallow it quickly. Then I crunch a bit of crispy, black stuff.

Mr Spinks rushes out to the kitchen. I can hear him being sick in the kitchen sink.

Dad stands up. It is too much for him. He cracks. 'Aaaaaagh,' he screams. He charges at me with hands held out like claws.

I run for it. I run down to my room and lock the door. Dad yells and shouts. He kicks and screams. But I lie low.

Tomorrow, when he calms down, I'll own up. I'll tell him how I went down the street and bought a new fly swat for fifty cents. I'll tell him about the currants and little bits of licorice that I smeared on the fly swat.

I mean, I wouldn't really eat dead flies. Not unless it was for something important anyway.

Illustrated by Bryan Poole

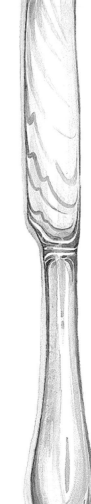

11

Telling Tales

TREVOR HARVEY

Setting   a primary classroom

Characters   teacher: a class of pupils, including Janice, Ali and Brian

Scenery and props   a chair, a bell

Production notes   Nine- to twelve-year-olds will enjoy the humour in this short play. The characters can be changed to suit the needs of individual classes.

A group of children gather on the carpet in the book corner. Their new teacher sits on a chair in front of them. She gradually gets more angry.

Teacher	As it's nearly time for the bell, if you all sit *very* quietly, I'll tell you a story …
All	GREAT!
Teacher	'Once upon a time …'
1st Pupil	Sorry, miss, we've heard it.
Teacher	I don't think so.
2nd Pupil	Yes we have, miss. We heard it last year in Mr Elton's class, didn't we?
All	YES!
3rd Pupil	Don't you know any other stories?
1st Pupil	Yeah, tell us a different one, miss.
Teacher	Oh, very well. 'Long, long ago …'
Janice	'… in a faraway land.' We've heard *that* one as well.
Teacher	But you can't have done, Janice! I was just about to make it up.

10

	Janice	Sorry, miss – someone's beaten you to it. NEXT!
	Teacher	'There was once a young woodcutter …'
20	**Ali**	'… who ended up marrying a princess and they both lived happily ever after.' BOR-ING!
	Teacher	Look, Ali. I'm sure you'll find –
	Janice	NEXT!
	Teacher	'On the edge of a dark, dark forest …'
	Janice	'… lived a poor shepherd boy who kissed a frog and broke the magic spell that had been put on it by an evil witch.'
	1st Pupil	YUK!
	Teacher	It was a *stag*.
30	**Janice**	An evil *stag*.
	Ali	Are you sure, miss?
	Teacher	No! The evil witch *put* a spell *on* the stag.
	2nd Pupil	Cor, the rotten toad! She's already put one on the frog.
	Teacher	She was NOT a toad and she HADN'T put a spell on the frog!
	Ali	You mean – it was a REAL frog?

	Teacher	Listen, everyone – there are NO frogs in my story, just a stag and a shepherd girl.
40	**Brian**	She's done it again, hasn't she, miss?
	Teacher	What ARE you talking about, Brian?
	Brian	That witch, miss. She's used another of her spells. It was a shepherd BOY a minute ago.
	Teacher	Nonsense! In MY story it has ALWAYS been a girl.
	2nd Pupil	Then you must be a bit muddled, miss.
50	**Teacher**	Of course I'm NOT muddled! In my story, you'll find out that the shepherd boy didn't kiss the stag because the stag turns into a handsome young MAN.
	Ali	It could be his brother …
	Janice	Or a footballer – they're always kissing!
	Brian	That's right, miss! It must be his long-lost footballing brother who got himself turned into a frog –
	Teacher	A STAG!
	Brian	– because his side were beating Spurs …
	3rd Pupil	Twelve nil …
60	**Ali**	In the Cup!
	Brian	That proves it, then. It must have been a frog, miss.
	Teacher	WHY must it have been a frog, Brian?
	Brian	Well, you couldn't get a stag in a cup, could you, miss?
	Janice	Then, one day, they see your shepherd girl …
	Brian	She turns out to be a talent scout for Liverpool.
70	**Janice**	She signs them all up – and they win game after game after game!

14

Illustrated by Keith Collman

Ali	But one day your woodcutter comes along, miss. He chops them in half.
Janice	He's an Arsenal supporter and he doesn't like Liverpool winning.
Ali	So, your evil witch sees what he's done –
3rd Pupil	She doesn't like football –
2nd Pupil	*Or* woodcutters!
Ali	And, as a punishment, she turns the beautiful princess into a referee!
Janice	The woodcutter doesn't love her any more, so they don't get married after all.

Bell rings for hometime.

Ali	Ohh, miss! There's the bell for hometime.
Brian	You'll have to finish telling us your story tomorrow.
Janice	I'm glad you're our new teacher, miss. You don't half tell interesting stories …
All	GREAT!

80

15

Abducted by Aliens

A SHORT PLAY BY IAN SOUTER

The scene is set in a television studio.

Presenter   Well, good evening, viewers and we've got quite a news-story for you tonight. It would appear that a local man, a certain Mr I. C. Stars, claims to have been abducted by aliens. So let's go straight over to our outside reporter, Luke Snappy. Are you there, Luke?

An outside location.

Reporter   I certainly am, Eamonn. And standing right next to me is a man who is ready to share his extraordinary story with us tonight. So perhaps you'd like to tell us where it all began.

Local Man   Well, I had just opened my eyes and there was this blinding light …

Reporter   From a spacecraft?

Local Man   No, my ceiling. You see I'd left the light on all night! Anyway, it was when I was getting dressed that there was a knocking at the front door.

Reporter   Ah! The aliens were trying to break down your front door!

Local Man   No, it was the postman with a parcel containing my new hearing aid. Wonderful little thing. Can even pick up Radio Two on it!

Reporter   Yes well …

Local Man   But it was just as I was closing the door when …

Reporter   When … you were suddenly abducted by aliens who whisked you off through outer space!

10

20

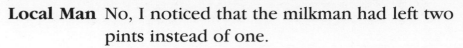

Local Man No, I noticed that the milkman had left two pints instead of one.

Reporter Excuse me, but have you or have you not been abducted by aliens?

The local man starts to shake his hearing aid.

Local Man Who's been constructed by Australians? I think it's the batteries you know! CONSTRUCTED BY AUSTRALIANS! What nonsense.

He shakes his hearing aid even harder.

Reporter Look, haven't you claimed to have been whisked off into outer space by aliens, through the galaxies to a far-distant planet.

Local Man No, mate! The furthest I've been today is Tesco's on the number 27 bus!

Reporter Now, let's start again. You are Mr I. C. Stars and this is number 19 Sydney Street?

Local Man Number 19? No this is number 16. The number 9 has slipped round into 6.

Reporter So where is number 19?

Local Man It's that house right across the street. The one with the flashing lights and the flying saucer above it.

The screen goes fuzzy and we return to the studio.

Presenter Yes, well, we seem to be having a little problem with interference at the moment so let's have the weather forecast for tomorrow.

The screen changes to a weather map.

What's going on! Luke Snappy that's a joke. Luke Stupid is more like it! He ought to be fired! Fired into outer space along with his ridiculous reports of aliens!

My Mother Saw a Dancing Bear

My mother saw a dancing bear
By the schoolyard, a day in June.
The keeper stood with chain and bar
And whistle-pipe, and played a tune.

And bruin lifted up its head
And lifted up its dusty feet,
And all the children laughed to see
It caper in the summer heat.

They watched as for the Queen it died.
They watched it march. They watched it halt.
They heard the keeper as he cried,
'Now, roly-poly! Somersault!'

And then, my mother said, there came
The keeper with a begging-cup,
The bear with burning coat of fur,
Shaming the laughter to a stop.

They paid a penny for the dance,
But what they saw was not the show;
Only, in bruin's aching eyes,
Far-distant forests, and the snow.

CHARLES CAUSLEY

Illustrated by Joan Martin May

18

What has Happened to Lulu?

What has happened to Lulu, mother?
    What has happened to Lu?
There's nothing in her bed but an old rag-doll
    And by its side a shoe.

Why is her window wide, mother,
    The curtain flapping free,
And only a circle on the dusty shelf
    Where her money-box used to be?

Why do you turn your head, mother,
    And why do the tear-drops fall?
And why do you crumple that note on the fire
    And say it is nothing at all?

I woke to voices late last night,
    I heard an engine roar.
Why do you tell me the things I heard
    Were a dream and nothing more.

I heard somebody cry, mother,
    In anger or in pain,
But now I ask you why, mother,
    You say it was a gust of rain.

Why do you wander about as though
    You don't know what to do?
What has happened to Lulu, mother?
    What has happened to Lu?

CHARLES CAUSLEY

Illustrated by Joan Martin May

Friend or Foe

Michael Morpurgo

Down in the hall everyone had stopped talking and Miss Roberts was speaking. 'The boys have all had a very long day, and I think we should get them off to bed as quickly as we can. But I know they'd all like me to thank you kind people for our welcoming meal. It's a long time since we've eaten like that. Now most of you are having one boy to stay and some two or three. Do choose quickly. They're a good bunch of boys, and I know you'll look after them as well as you can. You'll find their names and ages on their placards,

10 so as soon as you've chosen the one you're having, please register with Miss Evers at the table by the door. That way we'll know where everyone has gone to. It wouldn't do to lose anyone now, would it? Take the first row first and then the back row will move forward.'

The crowd of faces in the hall moved in closer, looking up at them. The children sat sipping their cocoa and gazed back down at them. There was a lot of whispering and it was a long time before anyone moved. Then one of the ladies stepped forward and peered closely for a moment at

20 Paul's placard. She smiled up at him over her glasses.

'Come on then, Paul,' she said, tapping him on the knee. 'Let's get the ball rolling. You come along with me.'

'Yes, miss,' said Paul and looked to Miss Roberts for reassurance. Miss Roberts nodded.

'Off you go then, Paul. And be good now.' Miss Roberts spoke kindly, and Paul got up and walked down the steps into the hall. The lady took his case and the two of them walked away towards Miss Evers' table at the back of the hall.

30 'Doesn't know what she's in for,' Tucky whispered from behind his cocoa mug. And David smiled for the first time that day. He sipped his cocoa and looked around the hall, trying to pick out a face he liked, but there were too many people and they were too remote to be real.

It was a smooth enough business after that. One by one the chairs on the platform emptied and soon the whole front row was gone. Miss Roberts beckoned the back row into their places.

Sam went. Billy Preston and Graham Watts went together, and gradually the hall was emptying. There was a small knot by the registration table, and Miss Roberts was with them. There was something wrong, David could tell that. Everyone kept glancing back up at the platform where David and Tucky sat side by side at the end of the front row. There was no one left.

'I'm sorry, Miss Roberts,' one of the ladies was saying. 'I'm sorry, but there's been an upset.'

'They have to sleep somewhere, don't they?' Miss Roberts sounded crisp. They were speaking in that urgent half-whisper that adults use when they don't want to alarm listening children.

''Tis Mr Reynolds out to Hamleigh Farm. He's not come in to collect. They were all told. Half past eight he was told, like the rest. 'Tis half past eleven now. Can't think where he's to.'

'But even with Mr Reynolds, that still leaves one boy unaccounted for,' Miss Roberts insisted.

'That'll be all right, you'll see, my dear. We'll find him somewhere. Poor little scrap.'

Tucky leaned closer to David. 'Davey, if they can't find anyone to look after us, will they send us home, d'you think?'

'Doubt it.'

'But what will they do with us then?'

'Miss Roberts will see us right,' David said hopefully. 'Don't worry, she'll see to it.'

'Davey. Why do you think no one chose us?' Tucky droned on in his flat voice.

'They didn't choose me, 'cos you were sitting next to me, and they didn't choose you because I was sitting next to you. And besides, we're not the prettiest in the class, are we?' He tried to joke it away, but he was hurt inside just as Tucky was. Time and time again people had looked him over and passed him by. 'Anyway,' he went on, 'didn't much like the look of them.'

'Nor me,' said Tucky. 'Nor me.'

The arguing at the other end of the hall had dwindled to an inaudible whisper now as they all realised the two boys might overhear them. But the longer it went on, the more obvious it became that the situation was serious. No one else seemed to have room for an evacuee, and it looked very much as if Mr Reynolds might not be coming at all. Finally Miss Roberts suggested they should give the boys a bed in the hall for the night, and someone went off to look for mattresses and blankets. Miss Hardy looked as if she would burst into tears at any minute, and Miss Evers kept throwing up her hands in disgust. Meanwhile David and Tucky sat alone up on the platform, too tired and bewildered even to care what happened to them.

They had pulled away the chairs to make room for the newly arrived mattresses and bedding when the hall door banged open. A huge, bearded man in a great woolly coat and knee-high gaiters strode into the hall followed by a rangy-looking black and white sheepdog. Everyone gawped.

'I'm sorry to be late, but I've come for a boy.'

'You are Mr Reynolds I
presume.' Miss Evers' voice was
stiff with anger.

'I am, my dear, and who may you be?'

'Mr Reynolds, these children have been
up for over fifteen hours now.' Miss Roberts
100   took Miss Evers' arm to try to stop her, but
Miss Evers would go on. 'They have travelled
nearly three hundred miles. You keep them
waiting for another two hours or more and all
you can say is you're sorry.'

Mr Reynolds looked down at Miss Evers. 'Lady,
I've said I'm sorry. There's nothing more I can say if that
won't satisfy you.' Then he looked up at the platform
and walked towards the two boys who had stood up
by this time. The dog followed and sat down by
110   Mr Reynolds' feet, looking up at them.

'Sorry to keep you,' he said, looking from one to the other. He had bright blue eyes and the lines on his face disappeared into a beard that was flecked with white at the chin. There was wet mud down the front of his coat and David noticed a broad gold wedding ring on his hand as he ruffled the dog's neck. ''Twas the mare that did it. She foaled just half an hour ago, and I couldn't leave her. She had a bit of trouble, always does, this one. But we managed between us, and 'tis a good-looking foal, another colt though. Five foals she's had, and not a filly among them.'

120

'Filly?' said Tucky. 'What's that?'

'Horse, my dear,' and Mr Reynolds' face creased into a smile. 'Filly's a girl horse. Colt's a boy, like yourself.'

'Mr Reynolds,' one of the village ladies came up beside him. 'Mr Reynolds, which one will you have?'

'Which one?'

'You put yourself down for one, Mr Reynolds. You said you only had room for one.'

'You want me to choose between these two boys, is that it?'

130

No one replied. He looked from David to Tucky and back again to David. ''Tis just like market day,' he said, shaking his head.

'Mr Reynolds!' Miss Evers stamped her foot in fury.

'This one's the fatter,' Mr Reynolds went on, looking at Tucky, 'but then this one's taller.' He reached out and gripped David's arm. 'He's a bit skinny, you know, not much meat on him.'

'Mr Reynolds, this is a serious matter,' said Miss Evers.

140

'You're right, lady, no doubt about it. 'Tis a serious matter. I'm supposed to look at two young lads, face to face mind you, and then pick out one and not the other. Right enough, that's serious. 'Tis revolting that's what 'tis. And what happens to the one I don't choose, eh? How d'you think he'll feel?'

'As a matter of fact,' said Miss Roberts quickly, 'we don't know what will happen to him.'

'You don't know!'

150 'Apparently there's been a mistake, a muddle over numbers, and one of these two boys has nowhere to go, not yet anyway. I don't suppose you'd consider taking them both on, would you? They're great friends at school, and we'd be very obliged.'

'Friends, are they?' Mr Reynolds considered the two boys carefully and read each of their placards slowly, stroking his dog all the time. 'I'll tell you one thing for certain, it'll be both of them or neither. There'll be no choosing. What about asking them? They might not like the look of me – have you thought of that?' No one said anything, so he

160 asked them direct. 'Well? What d'you think? I'm a farmer, forty-two years old, married, no children. My name's Jerry Reynolds, I run ninety-six acres – barley, sheep, milking cows, a few beef cattle and since the war began a few acres of potatoes. 'Tis only a small cottage, and you'll have to share one bed and do your bit about the farm. Well? What d'you say?'

Tucky looked at David and David looked back at him. It was the first good moment of the day – each understood instinctively what the other wanted.

170 'We'll go with you, mister,' David said.

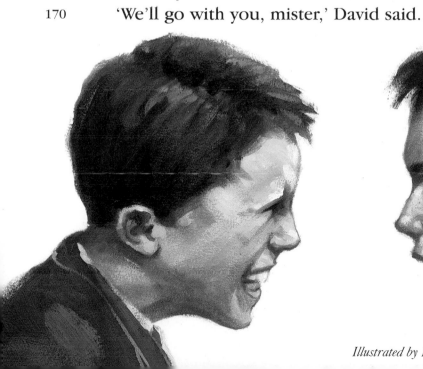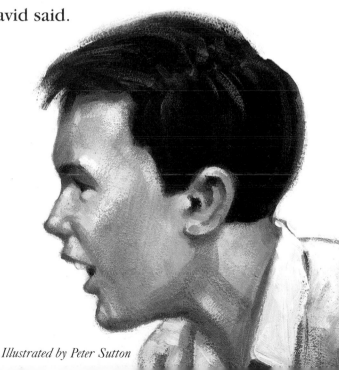

Illustrated by Peter Sutton

Up in the Attic

(and … something's … stirring …)

in the dark
in the dust
boxed Christmas lights
big tooth from a shark
sad rocking horse
a model Noah's Ark
cobwebby comics
doll's house painted green
dusty wine bottles
a bust of the Queen
leather-bound books
old sewing machine

Up in the attic …

Illustrated by Sholto Walker

and ... Down in the Cellar ...

Down in the cellar
brown boot in a box
remains of a cot
two brass mantel clocks
buckets and brushes
and musty old socks
damp pile of coal
and a splintered pine door
rusty rat trap
and a snaggle-toothed saw
six mildewy blankets
piled on the
stone floor

(and ... something's ... breathing ...)

WES MAGEE

THE CONCRETE POEM

What is a Concrete poem?
It doesn't sound quite right,
For concrete's rather heavy
And words are rather light.
Let's say you wrote a poem
'Ode to a concrete slab' –

A subject none too pretty,
Which many would call drab.
Perhaps you could describe it
As full of strength and grace,
And muse on what high tower
Might rest upon that base.
You may contrast its texture
With word and weathered stone
And wonder if it will some day
Be mellowed, creeper-grown.

But if you set the words out
And shape your poem, too,
To be the slab's three faces
With each face seen askew.
So that the poem's reader
Can look as well as hear,
Why then, your final poem
Is Concrete – is that clear?

NOEL PETTY

The Platform Arriving ...

Wheels cannot grip it!
Wheels cannot grip it!

Leaves leave wax
on the tracks

Why buy a ticket?
Why buy a ticket?

Train's a pain
late again

The diesel did it!
The diesel did it!

Work to rule
frozen fuel

Slippery slip-it!
Slippery slip-it

'Lectric fails
snow on rails

The platform arriving
will be on time ...

Steep incline
crash on line

No one to fix it
No one to fix it

Signal's stuck
just bad luck

GINA DOUTHWAITE

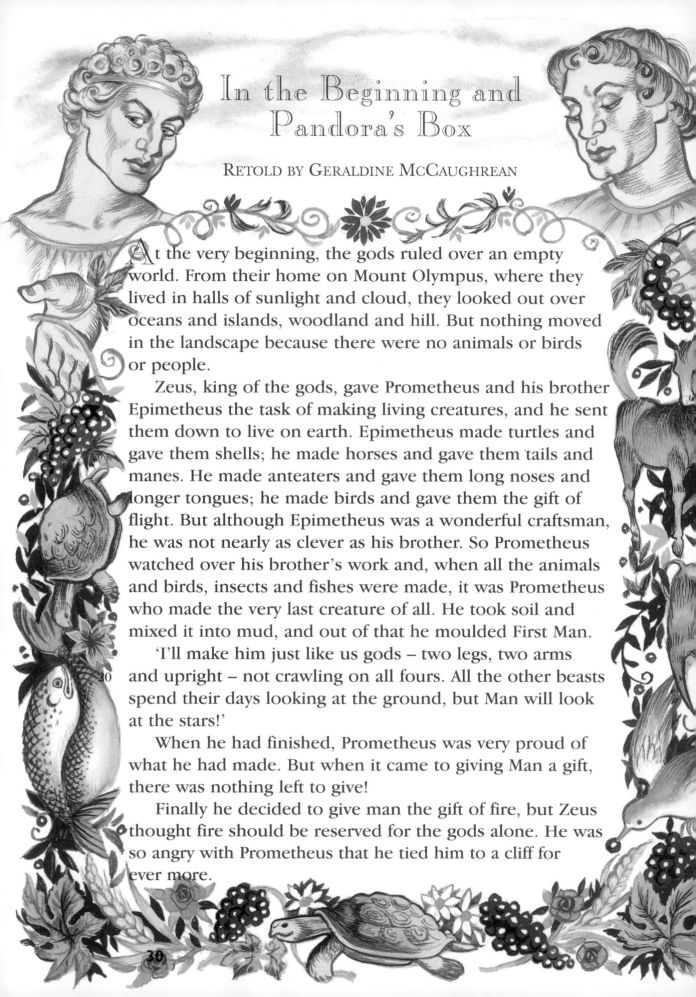

In the Beginning and Pandora's Box

RETOLD BY GERALDINE McCAUGHREAN

At the very beginning, the gods ruled over an empty world. From their home on Mount Olympus, where they lived in halls of sunlight and cloud, they looked out over oceans and islands, woodland and hill. But nothing moved in the landscape because there were no animals or birds or people.

Zeus, king of the gods, gave Prometheus and his brother Epimetheus the task of making living creatures, and he sent them down to live on earth. Epimetheus made turtles and gave them shells; he made horses and gave them tails and manes. He made anteaters and gave them long noses and longer tongues; he made birds and gave them the gift of flight. But although Epimetheus was a wonderful craftsman, he was not nearly as clever as his brother. So Prometheus watched over his brother's work and, when all the animals and birds, insects and fishes were made, it was Prometheus who made the very last creature of all. He took soil and mixed it into mud, and out of that he moulded First Man.

'I'll make him just like us gods – two legs, two arms and upright – not crawling on all fours. All the other beasts spend their days looking at the ground, but Man will look at the stars!'

When he had finished, Prometheus was very proud of what he had made. But when it came to giving Man a gift, there was nothing left to give!

Finally he decided to give man the gift of fire, but Zeus thought fire should be reserved for the gods alone. He was so angry with Prometheus that he tied him to a cliff for ever more.

30 Zeus was just as angry with Man for *accepting* the gift of fire, but you would never have thought so. He was busy making him another wonderful present.

With the help of the other gods, he shaped First Woman. Venus gave her beauty, Mercury gave her a clever tongue, Apollo taught her how to play sweet music. Finally Zeus draped a veil over her lovely head and named her Pandora.

Then, with a grin on his face, he sent for Epimetheus (who was not quite clever enough to suspect a trick).

'Here's a bride for you, Epimetheus – a reward for all your
40 hard work making the animals. And here's a wedding present for you both. But whatever you do, don't open it.'

The wedding present was a wooden chest, bolted and padlocked and bound with bands of iron. When he reached his home at the foot of Mount Olympus, Epimetheus set the chest down in a dark corner, covered it with a blanket, and put it out of his mind. After all, with Pandora for a bride, what more could a man possibly want?

In those days the world was a wonderful place to live. No one was sad. Nobody ever grew old or ill. And Epimetheus
50 married Pandora; she came to live in his house, and everything she wanted he gave her.

But sometimes, when she caught sight of the chest, Pandora would say, 'What a strange wedding present. Why can't we open it?'

'Never mind why. Remember, you must never touch it,' Epimetheus would reply sharply. 'Not touch at all. Do you hear?'

'Of course I won't touch it. It's only an old chest. What do I want with an old chest? ... What do you think is inside?'

60 'Never mind what's inside. Put it out of your mind.'

And Pandora did try. She really did. But one day, when Epimetheus was out, she just could not forget about the chest and somehow she found herself standing right beside it.

'No!' she told herself. 'I expect it's full of cloth – or dishes – or papers. Something dull.' She bustled about the house. She tried to read. Then ...

'*Let us out!*'

'Who said that?'

'Do let us out, Pandora!'

70 Pandora looked out of the window. But in her heart of hearts she knew that the voice was coming from the chest. She pulled back the blanket with finger and thumb. The voice was louder now: 'Please, please *do* let us out, Pandora!'

'I can't. I mustn't.' She crouched down beside the chest.

'Oh, but you *have* to. We *want* you to. We *need* you to, Pandora!'

'But I promised!' Her fingers stroked the latch.

'It's easy. The key's in the lock,' said the little voice – a purring little voice.

80 It was. A big golden key.

'No. No, I mustn't,' she told herself.

'But you do *want* to, Pandora. And why shouldn't you? It was your wedding present too, wasn't it? ... Oh, all right, don't let us out. Just peep inside. What harm can that do?'

Pandora's heart beat faster.

Click. The key turned.

Clack. Clack. The latches were unlatched.

BANG!

The lid flew back and Pandora was knocked over by an icy
90 wind full of grit. It filled the room with howling. It tore the curtains and stained them brown. And after the wind came slimy things, growling snarling things, claws and snouts, revolting things too nasty to look at, all slithering out of the chest.

'I'm Disease,' said one.

'I'm Cruelty,' said another.

'I'm Pain, and she's Old Age.'

'I'm Disappointment and he's Hate.'

'I'm Jealousy and that one there is War.'

100 'AND I AM DEATH!' said the smallest purring voice.

The creatures leapt and scuttled and oozed out through the windows, and at once all the flowers shrivelled, and the fruit on the trees grew mouldy. The sky itself turned a filthy yellow, and the sound of crying filled the town.

Mustering all her strength, Pandora slammed down the lid of the chest. But there was one creature inside.

'No, no, Pandora! If you shut me inside, that will be your worst mistake of all! Let me go!'

'Oh no! You don't fool me twice,' sobbed Pandora.

110 'But I am Hope!' whispered the little voice faintly. 'Without me the world won't be able to bear all the unhappiness you have turned loose!'

So Pandora lifted the lid, and a white flicker, small as a butterfly, flitted out and was blown this way and that by the howling winds. And as it fluttered through the open window, a watery sun came out and shone on the wilted garden.

Illustrated by Joan Martin May

JOAN
MARTIN
MAY

How Night Came to the World

A *story from the Amazon rainforest of Brazil*

RETOLD BY SEAN TAYLOR

People say that many, many years ago at the very beginning of the world, there were no animals, no birds, no fish. And, what's more, there was no night. The sun never stopped shining. It was always day.

Anyway, at that time there was a Great Snake who lived in a cave on the banks of the River Amazon and she had a daughter. This daughter was very beautiful, very magical, and she was married to the son of a village chief. But because there was no night, this husband of hers could
10 never sleep. He tossed, he turned, he sat up in his hammock, he lay down again, but he could not sleep a wink.

'Ai! Ai! Ai!' shouted the husband one day, 'It's too hot. It's too bright. How are we meant to sleep?'

'Calm yourself,' said his wife. 'We'll be able to sleep only when the first night comes to the world.'

'Well isn't there some way we can make this first night come to the world?'

His wife said, 'Night exists, but it is at the bottom of the
20 River Amazon. Only my mother, the Great Snake, knows where.'

So, they decided to send three boys to find the
Great Snake and ask her if she would make night
come to the world. The three boys took a canoe and rowed
up the river towards the Great Snake's dark cave. When
they got to the cave, the boys crept in, frozen with fear.

The cave was deep and damp. All around were scattered
broken canoes and chewed bones. And there, sleeping at
the very back of the cave, was the Great Snake. Her teeth
were as long as a man's arm. The boys came so close they
30 could feel the snake's breath warm on their faces.

'What is it?' she asked.

'Erm …' said the first boy. 'Are you the Great Snake?'

'Well who do you think I am? The Little Canary? Of
course I'm the Great Snake. Now what do you want?'

'Well,' said the second boy, 'your son-in-law can't sleep.
So your daughter, she sent us to see if maybe, well, perhaps
… perhaps …'

'Perhaps *what*, boy?' hissed the Great Snake. 'Speak up!'

'Perhaps you know how to make night come to the
40 world,' said the third boy.

The Great Snake whispered, 'Of course I know how to
make night come to the world.'

Then her great, thick body uncoiled past the boys,
dropped down into the river and disappeared. In a few
moments she was back, and in her mouth was a *tucumã*
palm-nut, sealed at one end with yellow wax. 'Take this,'
she said, giving the palm-nut to the first boy. 'This is what
my daughter wants. But be careful with it. Don't drop it.
Don't do anything silly or your journey will be wasted. Now
50 disappear.'

So the boys took the palm-nut, went back to their boat
and started to row home. But after a while, they began to
hear a sound they had never heard before. The first boy
said, 'What's that little sound?'

The second boy put the palm-nut to his ear and said,
'Listen! It seems to be coming from inside here. Maybe
there's something caught inside.'

The third boy listened. 'Let's have a peep inside,' he
60 said.

'No!' said the first boy. 'Remember what the Great Snake
told us.'

But at that moment the sound got louder and the third
boy said, 'Don't worry about that old snake. She
can't see us here. I'm going to open it.'

But as soon as he scratched away the wax, darkness
poured out of the nut, across the river, over the forest and
into the sky. And as everything went black, out flew the bat,
the owl, the rat, the cricket. And the rainforest began to
70 change. Sticks floating in the river turned into fish. Logs
turned into jaguars. Canoes turned into alligators. All the
animals were created. They filled the sky with their grunts,
their roars and their howls. And those boys were so scared,
they decided to wait on the river bank until day.

Meanwhile, back where they had come from, the Great Snake's daughter looked up into the black sky.

'Ai, ai, ai,' she muttered. 'Those boys have let out the night too soon.'

'Come and sleep!' called her husband.

80 But she shook her head. 'No. Now I have to find a way to make the night share the world with the day.'

She pulled out one of her hairs, found a twig and wrapped the hair carefully around it. She mixed different coloured paints from clay and berries. Then she painted the twig white and red, threw it in the air and it turned into a *cujubim* – the bird that calls for the day. The *cujubim* flew away into the forest.

She took another hair, another twig, painted them grey, threw them in the air and it turned into an *inhambu*, the

90 bird that calls for the night. The *inhambu* flew away into the forest. Then, in the same way, she created the parrot, the egret, the humming-bird, the toucan and all the birds of the forest. She said, 'Some of these birds will call for the night, and some of them will call for the day. And that way, day and night will share the world.'

Then the morning birds began to sing. The sun started to rise and night went to sleep at the bottom of the River Amazon.

It wasn't long before the three boys were back. The

100 Great Snake's daughter was furious. 'Look!' she said. 'You have yellow wax on your hands! You opened the palm-nut! You stuck your noses into something that was none of your business. And because of that you are going to jump from tree to tree for the rest of time!'

And with that she transformed them into the only animal that still had not been created. And that is why, until today, monkeys have waxy yellow hands. And that is why monkeys shriek every night when it starts to get dark. So that is how night first came to the world and that is how the story ends.

Illustrated by Sheila Moxley

37

The Fox and the Crane

RETOLD BY SEAN TAYLOR

One day a fox invited a crane to dinner. He liked to amuse himself at the expense of his guests, so the only food he provided was a thin soup served in a shallow dish. The fox had no difficulty in lapping up his soup, but the crane did. As much as she tapped her long, thin beak against the bowl, she could not manage to swallow a single drop of soup. She was just as hungry at the end of the meal as she had been at the beginning.

The fox professed his deep regret at seeing her eat so little. 'Oh dear,' he said, 'I do hope the soup was not too salty for your taste.' The crane did not answer. All she did was beg the fox to do her the honour of returning the visit the next day.

The fox accepted the invitation and arrived at the appointed hour. The crane greeted him kindly. The food smelt excellent, and the fox was looking forward to satisfying his keen appetite. But when dinner was served, the crane produced two jars with very tall, narrow necks. The fox looked the strange vessels up and down. The crane, with her long beak, ate the food quite easily, and soon her jar was empty. But the fox could only walk round and round his jar, licking at its neck and sniffing the delicious food inside.

The crane professed her deep regret at seeing the fox eat so little. The fox was angry, but went on his way without complaining. The crane had paid him back with his own coin.

Illustrated by Gill Platt

The Tortoise and the Baboon

RETOLD BY SEAN TAYLOR

One evening Tortoise was crawling along the path when he met Baboon.

'Hello, my friend,' said Baboon cheerfully. 'You look hungry. Come to my place for supper.'

Tortoise was very grateful. It was a steep, bumpy path, but the thought of a good supper kept him going.

'Bless my tail!' laughed Baboon, when Tortoise arrived. 'What a long time you've taken. It's almost tomorrow! But supper's ready. All you have to do is climb up and get it.'

Tortoise looked up. There were three pots wedged in the branches of a tree, high above his head. He knew he could never reach them and so did Baboon. Poor Tortoise had been tricked and he went home hungry.

A few days later Baboon received an invitation for supper at Tortoise's. He laughed at how quickly good-natured Tortoise had forgiven him, and set off down the path. It was the dry season when many bush-fires occur, and to get to Tortoise's place Baboon had to cross a field of blackened grass. When he arrived, Tortoise was stirring a pot of very savoury smelling food. 'Pleased to see you, my friend,' he said to Baboon. 'But dear me, didn't your mother ever teach you to wash your hands before meals?'

Baboon looked at his paws. They were completely black.

'Run along to the river and give them a rinse,' said Tortoise. 'Then you may eat.'

Baboon scampered away and washed his paws in the river. But he had to come back across the burnt grass and he arrived just as dirty as before. 'Bless my tail,' said Tortoise with his mouth full, 'that will never do! Go back. Do it properly! And get a move on – I've started eating.'

Poor Baboon went back to the river time and again, but because his paws were always black, Tortoise refused him any food. When Tortoise swallowed the last mouthful Baboon realized he had been tricked and left.

'That will teach you a lesson,' smiled Tortoise, who withdrew into his shell for a good night's sleep.

Illustrated by Gill Platt

Bedd Gelert

RETOLD BY STEPHEN CORRIN

In a remote little village in North Wales, a long, long time ago, there lived a prince named Llewellyn and his beautiful infant son. The mother had died in childbirth and so the prince lavished all his love and care on his only child. Prince Llewellyn also had a trusted faithful hound, named Gelert, who could sense the prince's devotion to the child and so was as protective of him as his master was, or even more so.

One morning, as the child was sleeping peacefully in its
10 cradle, Prince Llewellyn heard the sound of a hunting horn and the barking of hunting dogs nearby.

'A share of that hunt must be mine,' he thought, 'for I am the owner of this land.' So, calling Gelert and pointing to the cradle, he simply said, 'Look after my son, while I am away,' and left. The dog obediently lay down next to the sleeping child.

Before very long the hound's fine nostrils quivered. He could scent an enemy. And indeed there was a wolf nosing in at the doorway. Gelert, quick as lightning, leapt at the
20 beast and the next moment the two were locked in a life and death struggle. The baby went on sleeping peacefully, unaware of any danger, but the two creatures fought savagely, Gelert to protect the infant and the wolf to devour it, for it was ravenously hungry after days of futile roaming the hills and forests.

As they fought, blood splattered all over the walls and floor, and the wolf, getting nearer the scent of its intended prey, pushed the brave dog closer to the cradle. Panting furiously, the wolf thrust Gelert right at its base and
30 overturned it, bespattering the coverlets with blood. Miraculously, the baby continued to sleep soundly, ignorant of the mortal danger it was in and undisturbed by the ferocious growling and snarling of the two combatants. But Gelert, now sensing the imminent danger to his ward,

Illustrated by Graham Berry

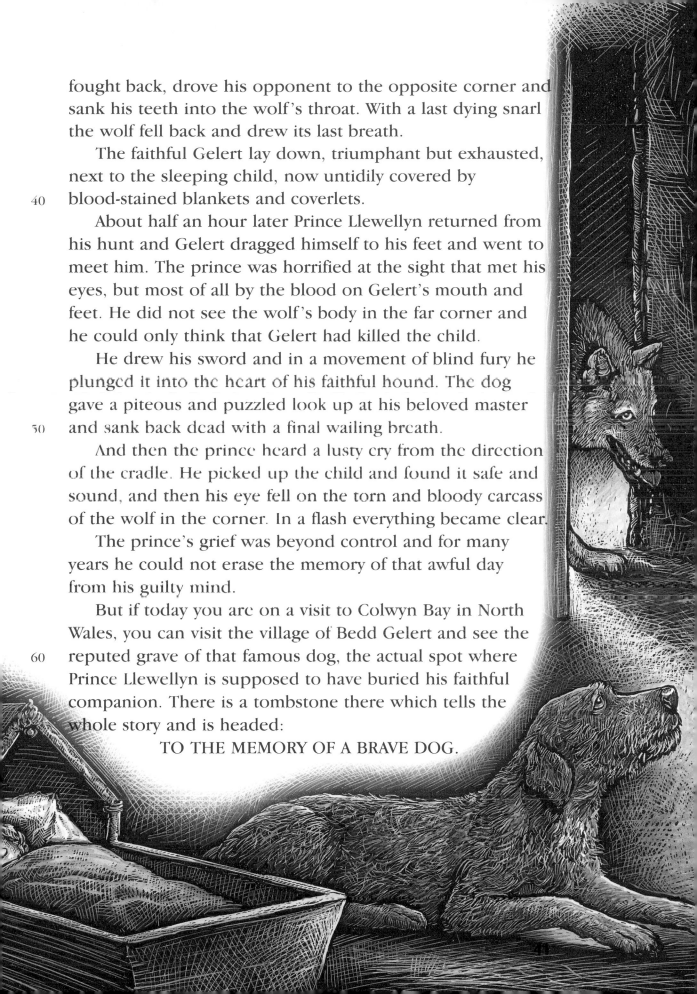

fought back, drove his opponent to the opposite corner and sank his teeth into the wolf's throat. With a last dying snarl the wolf fell back and drew its last breath.

The faithful Gelert lay down, triumphant but exhausted, next to the sleeping child, now untidily covered by blood-stained blankets and coverlets.

About half an hour later Prince Llewellyn returned from his hunt and Gelert dragged himself to his feet and went to meet him. The prince was horrified at the sight that met his eyes, but most of all by the blood on Gelert's mouth and feet. He did not see the wolf's body in the far corner and he could only think that Gelert had killed the child.

He drew his sword and in a movement of blind fury he plunged it into the heart of his faithful hound. The dog gave a piteous and puzzled look up at his beloved master and sank back dead with a final wailing breath.

And then the prince heard a lusty cry from the direction of the cradle. He picked up the child and found it safe and sound, and then his eye fell on the torn and bloody carcass of the wolf in the corner. In a flash everything became clear.

The prince's grief was beyond control and for many years he could not erase the memory of that awful day from his guilty mind.

But if today you are on a visit to Colwyn Bay in North Wales, you can visit the village of Bedd Gelert and see the reputed grave of that famous dog, the actual spot where Prince Llewellyn is supposed to have buried his faithful companion. There is a tombstone there which tells the whole story and is headed:

TO THE MEMORY OF A BRAVE DOG.

Beth Gêlert

That day Llewellyn little loved
    The chase of hart and hare;
And scant and small the booty proved,
    For Gêlert was not there.

Unpleased, Llewellyn homeward hied,
    When, near the portal seat,
His truant Gêlert he espied
    Bounding his lord to greet.

But when he gained the castle door,
    Aghast the chieftain stood;
The hound all o'er was smeared with gore;
    His lips, his fangs, ran blood.

Llewellyn gazed with fierce surprise;
    Unused such looks to meet,
His favourite checked his joyful guise,
    And crouched, and licked his feet.

Onward, in haste, Llewellyn passed.
    And on went Gêlert too;
And still, where'er his eyes he cast,
    Fresh blood-gouts shocked his view.

O'erturned his infant's bed he found.
    With blood-stained covert rent:
And all around the walls and ground
    With recent blood besprent.

He called his child – no voice replied –
    He searched with terror wild;
Blood, blood he found on every side,
    But nowhere found his child.

'Hell-hound! my child's by thee devoured,'
    The frantic father cried;
And to the hilt his vengeful sword
    He plunged in Gêlert's side.

Aroused by Gêlert's dying yell,
    Some slumberer wakened nigh;
What words the parent's joy could tell
    To hear his infant's cry!

Concealed beneath a tumbled heap
    His hurried search had missed,
All glowing from his rosy sleep
    The cherub boy he kissed.

No hurt had he, nor harm, nor dread,
    But, the same couch beneath,
Lay a gaunt wolf, all torn and dead,
    Tremendous still in death.

Ah, what was then Llewellyn's pain!
    For now the truth was clear;
His gallant hound the wolf had slain
    To save Llewellyn's heir.

WILLIAM ROBERT SPENCER

Illustrated by Graham Berry

The Highwayman

The wind was a torrent of darkness among the gusty trees,
The moon was a ghostly galleon tossed upon cloudy seas,
The road was a ribbon of moonlight over the purple moor,
And the highwayman came riding –
    Riding – riding –
The highwayman came riding, up to the old inn-door.

He'd a French cocked-hat on his forehead, a bunch of lace at his chin,
A coat of claret velvet, and breeches of brown doe-skin;
They fitted with never a wrinkle. His boots were up to the thigh!
And he rode with a jewelled twinkle,
    His pistol butts a-twinkle,
His rapier hilt a-twinkle, under the jewelled sky.

Over the cobbles he clattered and clashed in the dark inn-yard,
He tapped with his whip on the shutters, but all was locked and barred;
He whistled a tune to the window, and who should be waiting there
But the landlord's black-eyed daughter,
    Bess, the landlord's daughter,
Plaiting a dark red love-knot into her long black hair.

And in the dark old inn-yard a stable-wicket creaked
Where Tim the ostler listened. His face was white and peaked.
His eyes were hollows of madness, his hair like mouldy hay,
But he loved the landlord's daughter,
    The landlord's red-lipped daughter.
Dumb as a dog he listened, and he heard the robber say –

'One kiss, my bonny sweetheart, I'm after a prize to-night,
But I shall be back with the yellow gold before the morning light;
Yet, if they press me sharply, and harry me through the day,
Then look for me by moonlight,
    Watch for me by moonlight,
I'll come to thee by moonlight,
though hell should bar the way.'

He rose upright in the stirrups. He scarce could reach her hand,
But she loosened her hair i' the casement! His face burnt like a brand
As the black cascade of perfume came tumbling over his breast;
And he kissed its waves in the moonlight,
    (Oh, sweet black waves in the moonlight!)
Then he tugged at his rein in the moonlight, and galloped away to the
    west.

He did not come in the dawning. He did not come at noon;
And out o' the tawny sunset, before the rise o' the moon,
A red-coat came marching –
    Marching – marching –
King George's men came marching, up to the old inn-door.

They said no word to the landlord. They drank his ale instead.
But they gagged his daughter, and bound her, to the foot of her narrow bed.
Two of them knelt at her casement, with muskets at their side!
There was death at every window;
    And hell at one dark window;
For Bess could see, through her casement, the road that he would ride.

They had tied her up to attention, with many a sniggering jest.
They had bound a musket beside her, with the muzzle beneath her
    breast!
'Now, keep good watch!' and they kissed her.
    She heard the dead man say –
Look for me by moonlight;
    Watch for me by moonlight;
I'll come to thee by moonlight, though
hell should bar the way!

She twisted her hands behind her; but all the knots held good!
She writhed her hands till her fingers were wet with sweat or blood!
They stretched and strained in the darkness, and the hours crawled by
    like years,
Till, now, on the stroke of midnight,
    Cold, on the stroke of midnight,
The tip of one finger touched it! The trigger at least was hers!

The tip of one finger touched it. She strove no more for the rest.
Up, she stood up to attention, with the muzzle beneath her breast.
She would not risk their hearing; she would not strive again;
For the road lay bare in the moonlight;
    Bland and bare in the moonlight;
And the blood of her veins, in the moonlight, throbbed to her love's
    refrain.

Tlot-tlot; tlot-tlot! Had they heard it? The horse-hoofs ringing clear;
Tlot-tlot; tlot-tlot, in the distance! Were they deaf that they did not hear?
Down the ribbon of moonlight, over the brow of the hill,
    The highwayman came riding, Riding, riding!
The red-coats looked to their priming! She stood up, straight and still.
Tlot-tlot, in the frosty silence! Tlot-tlot, in the echoing night!

Nearer he came and nearer. Her face was like a light.
Her eyes grew wide for a moment; she drew one last deep breath,
Then her finger moved in the moonlight,
    Her musket shattered the moonlight,
Shattered her breast in the moonlight and warned him –
    with her death.

He turned. He spurred to the west; he did not know who stood
Bowed, with her head o'er the musket, drenched with her own red blood!
Not till the dawn he heard it, and his face grew grey to hear
How Bess, the landlord's daughter,
    The landlord's black-eyed daughter,
Had watched for her love in the moonlight, and died in the darkness there.

Back, he spurred like a madman, shouting a curse to the sky,
With the white road smoking behind him and his rapier brandished
    high
Blood-red were his spurs i' the golden noon; wine-red was his
    velvet coat;
When they shot him down on the highway,
    Down like a dog on the highway,
And he lay in his blood on the highway, with the bunch of lace at his throat.

And still of a winter's night, they say, when the wind is in the trees,
When the moon is a ghostly galleon tossed upon cloudy seas,
When the road is a ribbon of moonlight over the purple moor,
A highwayman comes riding –
    Riding – riding –
A highwayman comes riding, up to the old inn-door.

Over the cobbles he clatters and clangs in the dark inn-yard.
And he taps with his whip on the shutters, but all is locked and barred.
He whistles a tune to the window, and who should be waiting there
But the landlord's black-eyed daughter,
    Bess, the landlord's daughter,
Plaiting a dark red love-knot into her long black hair.

ALFRED NOYES

Illustrated by Ron Tiner

A Smuggler's Song

If you wake at midnight, and hear a horse's feet
Don't go drawing back the blind, or looking in the street.
Them that asks no questions isn't told a lie.
Watch the wall, my darling, while the Gentlemen go by!
      Five and twenty ponies,
      Trotting through the dark –
      Brandy for the Parson,
      'Baccy for the Clerk;
      Laces for a lady, letters for a spy,
And watch the wall, my darling, while the Gentlemen go by!

Running round the woodlump if you chance to find
Little barrels, roped and tarred, all full of brandy-wine,
Don't you shout to come and look, nor use 'em for your play.
Put the brushwood back again – and they'll be gone next day!

If you see a stable-door setting open wide;
If you see a tired horse lying down inside;
If your mother mends a coat cut about and tore;
If the lining's wet and warm – don't you ask no more!

If you meet King George's men, dressed in blue and red,
You be careful what you say, and mindful what is said.
If they call you 'pretty maid', and chuck you 'neath the chin,
Don't you tell where no one is, nor yet where no one's been!

Knocks and footsteps round the house – whistles after dark –
You've no call for running out till the house-dogs bark.
Trusty's here, and *Pincher*'s here, and see how dumb they lie –
They don't fret to follow when the Gentlemen go by!

If you do as you've been told, 'likely there's a chance,
You'll be give a dainty doll, all the way from France,
With a cap of Valenciennes, and a velvet hood –
A present from the Gentlemen, along o' being good!
 Five and twenty ponies,
 Trotting through the dark –
 Brandy for the Parson,
 'Baccy for the clerk.
Them that asks no questions isn't told a lie –
Watch the wall, my darling, while the Gentlemen go by!

RUDYARD KIPLING

Illustrated by Emma Chichester Clarke

49

Beauty and the Beast

RETOLD BY DENNIS HAMLEY

Once upon a time there was a merchant who had fallen upon hard times. His only comfort was his daughter, Beauty, whose nature was as lovely as her face.

One day, the merchant travelled to the city hoping to restore some of his former fortune. Before he left, he said to Beauty, 'Soon I'll be rich again I'll buy you anything you want.'

'I want nothing more than a single rose,' Beauty replied.

The city, though, was a hard place and the merchant was cheated out of what little he still possessed. Miserably he started the long journey home with no fortune and not even a rose for Beauty. Snow fell, harsh winds blew and the merchant lost his way in a great forest. Exhausted and frozen, he sank to the ground ready to die.

Suddenly he caught sight of lights in the distance. He struggled on and found a great palace. Inside he met no-one, but as if waiting for him, was good food, a warm bed and new clothes. Next morning, as he rode away through the palace grounds he passed a rose garden and, remembering Beauty, picked one of the lovely blooms.

Immediately, he heard a frightening roar. He turned and there stood a terrible Beast. It had huge yellow teeth and wild eyes which glowed with anger. 'So you repay my kindness with theft,' the Beast roared. 'For this you will die.'

'Forgive me,' cried the merchant. 'The rose was a gift for my daughter.'

'Then I'll spare you on one condition,' said the Beast. 'Your daughter must come to live with me here in my palace. If not you will die.'

When he returned home the merchant gave Beauty the rose and told her of the Beast's demands. 'Of course, I'll never let you go,' said the merchant. But Beauty insisted on going, knowing that if she failed to do so her father would die.

With a heavy heart she set off on her journey. When she first saw the Beast he was as terrifying as her father had described. But wonder of wonders the Beast did not kill Beauty. Instead he gave her a life of luxury. Her room was full of fine furniture and nothing was finer than a huge mirror. When she looked in it, she caught her breath in surprise. This mirror was magic and in it she saw her own house and her father sitting sadly by the fire.

As time passed Beauty conquered her fear and grew to like the Beast. Every day the Beast asked, 'Beauty, will you marry me?' Each time, Beauty answered, 'Beast, although I like you I cannot love you. But we can always be friends.' The Beast sighed. 'Then I must be content. But, please, Beauty, never leave me.'

One day, Beauty looked at her magic mirror and saw her father was very ill. She ran to the Beast. 'I must go to my father,' she cried.

'Very well,' the Beast answered unwillingly. 'But you must return in a week or I shall die of sorrow.'

Once at home, though, there was so much to do that ten days passed before she knew it. Then one night she dreamt that the Beast was close to death. Beauty awoke feeling such love and sadness for the Beast that she knew she must go to him at once.

When she arrived at the palace she found the Beast lying in the rose garden. 'Beast, don't die,' she cried. 'Now I know I really love you.' She bent and kissed him and immediately the Beast disappeared. Instead, there lay a prince so handsome that it took her breath away.

'Beauty,' he said. 'Years ago I was condemned to this terrible enchantment of ugliness until a beautiful woman consented to marry me. Your love has released me. Now I can take my rightful place in the world with you beside me as my wife.' So they were married and Beauty's father came to live with them in the palace. Beauty and her handsome prince lived happily ever after.

Illustrated by Greg Becker

51

Billy Beast **A seriously silly story**

LAURENCE ANHOLT

Betty and Benjamin Beast were very proud of their castle. They thought it was the most wonderful building for miles around. It had taken them years to get it just right with lovely green mouldy walls and black puddles in the corridors. There were damp, dark bedrooms with snails on the pillows, and smelly cellars too. At weekends, you would always find Benjamin up a stepladder whistling happily as he hung new cobwebs in corners or painted fresh mud on the ceilings.

There was only one thing that Betty and Benjamin were more proud of than their home, and that was their fine young son, Billy Beast. They loved Billy more than words can say.

By the time he was sixteen Billy had grown into a fine-looking beast. He was tall and strong with plenty of fleas in his hair and the sharpest brown teeth a beast could wish for. There wasn't a girl beast around who wasn't in love with young Billy. But as far as Benjamin and Betty were concerned, it would have to be a very special girl beast who could be disgusting enough to marry their son.

Then one morning, Benjamin and Betty went out gathering frog spawn for lunch, leaving young Billy playing quietly with his toad in his bedroom. Billy heard a noise outside, and when he looked out of the window he saw an old man wandering about in their beautiful weedy garden. The man had tied his horse to the tree and was busy *stealing* some of Betty's prize-winning roses!

'Hoi! What do you think you're doing?' shouted Billy. 'This is a private castle, you know. My mum will eat you if she catches you here.'

When the man looked up at the castle and saw young Billy Beast all hairy and horrid with a big toad sitting on his head he was *absolutely terrified*! 'Oh, p-please don't eat me, Mr Beast,' he stammered. 'I got lost and … and I promised my beautiful daughter I would bring her a red rose and …'

'Well, not from our garden, pal!' snorted Billy.

The man was so frightened that he promised that he would send his daughter, Beauty, to marry Billy if he was 40 allowed to go free.

'All right,' Billy agreed, 'but she'd better come soon or my dad will be after you too.'

'I … I'll send her straight away,' said the poor man, jumping on to his horse.

'And she'd better be as beautiful as you say,' Billy called after him.

'Oh yes, oh yes, she is!' shouted the man, riding away as fast as he could. 'There's nothing in the world more beautiful than my daughter.'

50 'What? More beautiful than my toad?' called Billy.

But the man was already out of sight.

When Betty and Benjamin came home, Billy told them the whole story.

'I'm going to be married,' he grunted happily, 'to the most beautiful girl in the world – the man said there's nothing in the world more beautiful than Beauty.'

Betty and Benjamin were very pleased to think of their son married to the most beautiful girl in the world, although they found it hard to believe that anyone could be 60 quite as good-looking as their Billy.

Early next morning, Beauty arrived. Billy saw her horse coming up the hill towards the castle. He ran to the mirror to make sure his teeth were nice and black and he checked that his breath was good and smelly. He splashed a little skunk juice under his arms, then he ran to the door to meet his bride.

Billy was very excited. As the doorbell rang, he twisted his face into the most beautifully disgusting shape that he could manage, then pulled open the door.

70 She was hardly hairy at all, except on her head. And her *teeth* – they were all sort of white and shiny! She had a horrid pink *nose* where her snout should be, and little *fingers* instead of nice claws! UGH! It was *disgusting*! 'I bet she hasn't even got a hairy chest,' thought Billy in dismay.

When Beauty saw Billy, she almost fainted on the spot. Billy could understand that, because his handsome looks often made girls feel weak at the knees. What he couldn't understand was that Beauty wasn't beautiful! In fact she looked just like an ordinary *girl*!

80 Betty and Benjamin were also disappointed, but they tried not to show it. The poor girl had come a long way to marry their son and she seemed upset too.

'I'm sure she will look better once we get rid of that nasty white dress and pop her into a nice sloppy mud bath,' said Betty kindly.

'And she'll probably get hairier as she gets older,' suggested Benjamin. 'Perhaps she hasn't been eating a healthy diet – I expect she's hungry now after that long journey. Let's start her off with a lovely bowl of warm

90 earwax and slug juice.'

So Betty and Benjamin set about trying to make Beauty a little more beastly, and Billy went into the garden with his toad and sulked.

After a few days, Beauty began to get used to living with the Beasts, and Billy had to admit that she was looking a little better; at least she was getting more smelly.

But then Beauty would go and spoil it all by doing something revolting like washing her hands before a meal, or combing her hair and everyone realised that no matter how they tried, Beauty would never be truly disgusting.

Billy promised his parents that he would try to get along with her, although he swore he would never marry her. He patiently taught her to burp nicely and to dribble, but she was slow to learn.

Then one morning in the garden, something horrid happened. Billy had just allowed Beauty to play with his toad when she turned around and tried to *kiss* him! He wiped his mouth and jumped away.

110 Beauty began to cry. 'I can't help it!' she wailed, 'I can't help looking like this. Of course I would like to be hairy and horrid like you. But couldn't you try to love me for what I am instead of the way I look?'

Now Billy was really a kind-hearted beast. He began to feel sorry for Beauty. He saw that she was right. It doesn't really matter what you look like, it's the person inside that counts. Before he knew what he was doing, Billy had put down his toad and taken Beauty into his hairy arms, he put his snout close to her little head and … SMACK! He kissed her tiny snubby nose.

120 Right before Billy's yellow eyes, Beauty began to change! She grew hairier and hairier. Her teeth grew brown and longer. Her fingers turned into beautiful claws! At last she stood before him – a truly wonderful beastie girl, with the most gorgeous damp snout Billy had ever seen, and a delightful smell of old socks and kangaroo sweat.

Beauty explained that the man who had stolen the roses was not her father, but a wicked wizard who had cast a spell on her. She would lose her beastly looks until the day someone like Billy was kind enough to kiss her and break 130 the spell.

Billy was so happy, he didn't know what to say, so he just dribbled a little. The beastly couple skipped happily up the steps of the castle, claw in claw, burping excitedly to each other.

And they were all disgustingly happy for the rest of their beastly lives.

Illustrated by Arthur Robbins

Grandpa Chatterji

JAMILA GAVIN

Mum was scurrying about. Dad was fiddling with his tie. He always fiddled with his tie when he was nervous. Neetu and Sanjay looked a little solemn. Today Neetu was wearing a dress and Sanjay was wearing grey trousers and a jacket.

Grandpa Chatterji was still only wearing his *dhoti*. He had done his yoga exercises, he had bathed, he had cleaned his teeth, he had washed out his mouth and nose and throat by gargling and snorting with salt water, and he had said his prayers.

10 When he came down to breakfast, his face was shining with cleanliness and good humour, and he was surprised to notice that everyone looked a little glum.

'What is happening?' he asked. 'Why the long faces?' He looked at his grandchildren. 'Is something wrong?'

'Didn't you know?' cried Neetu. 'Grandpa Leicester is visiting us today! You'd better get dressed.'

'I am dressed,' corrected Grandpa Chatterji.

'Grandpa Leicester will call you "jungly" if you don't put on a suit,' said Neetu doubtfully.

20 'Don't worry, Grandpa Leicester won't find anything wrong with me when we meet,' replied Grandpa Chatterji, reassuringly.

'I must start preparing food,' murmured Mother. 'Grandpa Leicester is rather fussy about what he eats.'

'Why don't you leave the cooking to me. Relax, have a bath, and put on your best sari,' suggested Grandpa Chatterji soothingly. 'Leave the food to me!'

Mum shrugged with defeat and fled. 'Don't blame me if the meal is ruined and Grandpa Leicester never comes here
30 again!' she wailed to her husband.

56

'Now then, I need a hand,' said Grandpa Chatterji. 'All these vegetables need washing and chopping up. I want the potatoes and carrots diced into small chunks; I want the cauliflower broken into little flowers and someone is going to have to slice the onions.'

'I'll do it!' shouted Neetu eagerly.

'I'll do it!' yelled Sanjay.

The kitchen came alive with smells. Smoke and steam poured out through the doors and windows. Grandpa chopped and sliced and tossed and fried and rolled. A big saucepan of fat smoked to boiling point on the gas ring. A large mixing bowl full of batter stood nearby all lumpy with chopped-up vegetables. Grandpa was just about to ladle out a portion of batter and drop it, sizzling into the fat, when the doorbell rang.

'Oh, no!' exclaimed the children. 'Grandpa Leicester has arrived already!'

They peeped into the hall and saw Dad opening the front door. 'Father! It's you!' came his voice. 'You're early. We weren't expecting you so soon.'

They saw Grandpa Leicester standing there so smart and stern. He wore a dark grey pinstriped suit; he wore a pure white French shirt with a stiff collar and cuffs which showed exactly two inches beneath the sleeve of his jacket; he had on his smart Rotary Club tie, and on his feet were shiny, mirror-bright black Italian leather shoes.

'Look!' hissed Sanjay. 'Grandpa Leicester's come in his new Jaguar. Do you think he'll take us for a ride?' He stared longingly beyond his grandfather to the beautiful, sleek, low, dark-green saloon car which crouched in the road.

'Shouldn't think so,' muttered Neetu. 'Not after you went and got chocolate all over the seats of his last car.'

They heard Mum coming downstairs, swishing and tinkling. She had put on one of her best saris and wore her bangles and earrings. Grandpa Leicester remarked admiringly, 'Oh, don't you look lovely, my dear!'

'Welcome, *Papaji*!' Mother murmured. 'I do hope you had an uneventful journey.'

'Well! Where is everybody? Where is Chatterji *sahib*?' Grandpa Leicester demanded, stepping inside. 'And where are my grandchildren?'

Grandpa Leicester immediately strode to the kitchen and flung open the door. 'So, my little ones! You are hiding in here, are you? he cried jovially, then stopped with astonishment. There before him stood Grandpa Chatterji, Neetu and Sanjay all covered in batter and flour looking like white ghosts, and wishing that, like spirits, they could disappear.

If there was one thing Grandpa Leicester couldn't bear, it was mess. They could tell by the critical way his eyes swept around, that he could see nothing but mess; messy children, messy kitchen and a messy Grandpa Chatterji. With sinking hearts, they waited to hear his severe voice telling them off. 'I don't like my grandchildren to look messy.'

Mum looked as if she wished she could disappear through the floor. 'Sanjay! Look at your best jacket and trousers! Neetu! Look at the state of your beautiful dress! Oh, Pa! How could you let these children get into such a mess?' she accused Grandpa Chatterji.

'We've been cooking,' exclaimed Grandpa Chatterji, undaunted. Then he strode up to Grandpa Leicester with a broad, beaming face and clasped him in his arms. 'How good to see you again!'

'Hey, hey!' cried Grandpa Leicester, aghast, and pulled himself away from Grandpa Chatterji's floury embrace. 'Oh, no! Look at my best suit!'

Everyone stared in horror at the white imprints of hands on each of Grandpa Leicester's dark, pinstriped shoulders.

Mum grabbed Neetu and Sanjay and fled upstairs.

'Ma,' whispered Neetu fearfully. 'What will Grandpa Leicester do to Grandpa Chatterji?'

'I don't know,' she answered in a shaky voice. 'Perhaps he'll just go home again.'

Time passed. The two grandfathers were still in the kitchen behind closed doors. Neetu and Sanjay had cleaned themselves up and changed their clothes; Dad sat uneasily in the living room, while Mum paced up and down imagining that lunch would be a total disaster.

'When are we going to eat?' moaned Neetu.

'I'm starving!' groaned Sanjay.

Suddenly, the two grandfathers appeared in the doorway. Grandpa Chatterji was still in his *dhoti* with an overall on top, and Grandpa Leicester – everyone looked in amazement at Grandpa Leicester. He had taken off his pinstriped jacket, removed his smart Rotarian tie and rolled up the sleeves of his sparkling white French shirt. Most incredible of all, he had tied a frilly pinny round his waist. 'Lunch is served!' they both exclaimed, beaming with delight.

What a feast the two grandfathers had prepared. The table was overflowing with food. There were bowls of

pakoras, plates of *pooris*, tureens of turmeric-coloured lentils and dark green spinach. There was casseroles of vegetables and egg curries, saucers of pickles, dishes of yoghurt and chopped cucumber, and platters piled high with snow-white rice.

130　　'Eat, eat!' begged the grandfathers, passing round the plates.

Everybody ate. Nobody really spoke, except to exclaim, 'Delicious! Wonderful! Can I have another *pakora*? You two should open a restaurant!'

They seemed to eat all afternoon till there was barely a dish which hadn't been scraped clean. Then Mum, Dad and the children said they would do the washing up.

Grandpa Leicester stuck his thumbs in the waist of his trousers and said, 'I've eaten too much and my trousers are

140　　too tight.' Then he looked enviously at Grandpa Chatterji. 'I do like your *dhoti*. It's years since I wore one.'

'I have a spare one in my room,' beamed Grandpa Chatterji. 'Please come up and put it on.'

When the children had finished helping in the kitchen they went looking for their grandpas. The house was strangely quiet. Where were they? Perhaps they were snoozing in front of the television; but there was no one in the living room. Perhaps they were sitting in the garden; but there was no one in the garden.

150　　They went upstairs. Grandpa Chatterji's bedroom door was a little ajar. Neetu and Sanjay quietly peered inside. Then they looked at each other and hunched their shoulders in secret laughter. Grandpa Leicester had taken off his uncomfortable pinstriped suit, his French shirt and his Rotarian tie. He had taken off his stiff, shining black

60

leather Italian shoes. His chest was bare and his legs and feet were bare. All he wore was a thin cotton *dhoti*, and he sat cross-legged next to Grandpa Chatterji on his special Indian carpet. Their eyes were shut and their faces were serene and they breathed in for a very long time … and out for a very long time.

'What are you doing, Grandpa?' whispered Neetu.

'We're digesting,' said Grandpa Leicester.

'And meditating,' said Grandpa Chatterji.

'When you've finished digesting and meditating, will you take us for a ride in your new Jaguar?' whispered Sanjay tentatively.

'Jaguar?' asked Grandpa Chatterji, opening one eye. 'I've heard of riding *on* an elephant or being pulled *by* a horse, but I've never heard of riding *in* a jaguar.'

'You've never heard of riding in a Jaguar?' asked Grandpa Leicester, opening one eye. Then he opened his other eye. 'Shall we take Grandpa Chatterji for a ride in a Jaguar?' he asked his grandchildren with a wink.

They all went downstairs. They opened the door. There was the Jaguar waiting for them all glossy and shining.

'Ah!' Grandpa Chatterji gave a heartfelt sigh at the beauty of the machine. 'So that is what you call a jaguar! Yes, let's carry on with our digesting in a Jaguar.'

'I think I'd better put on my shoes,' said Grandpa Leicester. 'I can't drive barefoot.' So he put on his black, shiny, Italian shoes. They looked a little odd with a *dhoti*, but nobody cared. They sank into the soft leathery seats. Grandpa Leicester turned the key. The car roared into life with throbbing power. Then they sped down the road, silent and swift as a jungle cat.

Illustrated by Rosalind Hudson

The Mouth-organ Boys

JAMES BERRY

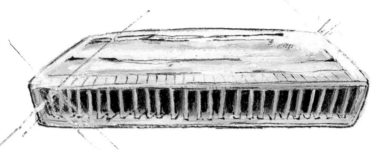

I wanted a mouth-organ, I wanted it more than anything else in the whole world. I told my mother. She kept ignoring me but I still wanted a mouth-organ badly.

I was only a boy. I didn't have a proper job. Going to school was like a job but nobody paid me to go to school. Again I had to say to my mother, 'Mam, will you please buy a mouth-organ for me?'

It was the first time now that my mother stood and answered me properly. Yet listen to what my mother said.

10   'What d'you want a mouth-organ for?'

'All the other boys have a mouth-organ, Mam,' I told her.

'Why is that so important? You don't have to have something just because others have it.'

'They won't have me with them without a mouth-organ, Mam,' I said.

'They'll soon change their minds, Delroy.'

'They won't, Mam. They really won't. You don't know Wildo Harris. He never changes his mind. And he never lets any other boy change his mind either.'

20   'Delroy, I haven't got the time to argue with you. There's no money to buy a mouth-organ. I bought you new shoes and clothes for Independence Celebrations. Remember?'

'Yes, Mam.'

'Well, money doesn't come on trees.'

'No, Mam.' I had to agree.

'It's school-day. The sun won't stand still for you. Go and feed the fowls. Afterwards milk the goat. Then get yourself ready for school.'

She sent me off. I had to go and do my morning jobs.

30   Oh my mother never listened! She never understood anything. She always had reasons why she couldn't buy me something and it was no good wanting to talk to my dad. He always cleared off to work early.

    All my friends had a mouth-organ, Wildo, Jim, Desmond, Len – everybody had one, except me. I couldn't go round with them now. They wouldn't let anybody go round with them without a mouth-organ. They were now 'The Mouth-organ Boys'. And we used to be all friends. I used to be their friend. We all used to play games together, and have

40 fun together. Now they pushed me away.

    'Delroy! Delroy!' my mother called.

    I answered loudly. 'Yes, Mam!'

    'Why are you taking so long feeding the fowls?'

    'Coming, mam.'

    'Hurry up, Delroy.'

    Delroy. Delroy. Always calling Delroy!

    I milked the goat. I had breakfast. I quickly brushed my teeth. I washed my face and hands and legs. No time left and my mother said nothing about getting my mouth-organ.

50 But my mother had time to grab my head and comb and brush my hair. She had time to wipe away toothpaste from my lip with her hand. I had to pull myself away and say, 'Good day, Mam.'

    'Have a good day, Delroy,' she said, staring at me.

    I ran all the way to school. I ran wondering if the Mouth-organ Boys would let me sit with them today. Yesterday they didn't sit next to me in class.

    I was glad the boys came back. We all sat together as usual. But they teased me about not having a mouth-organ.

60   Our teacher, Mr Goodall, started writing on the blackboard. Everybody was whispering. And it got to everybody talking quite loudly. Mr Goodall could be really cross. Mr Goodall had big muscles. He had a moustache too. I would like to be like Mr Goodall when I grew up. But he could be really cross. Suddenly Mr Goodall turned

round and all the talking stopped, except for the voice of Wildo Harris. Mr Goodall held the chalk in his hand and stared at Wildo Harris. He looked at Teacher and dried up. The whole class giggled.

70   Mr Goodall picked out Wildo Harris for a question. He stayed sitting and answered.

'Will you please stand up when you answer a question?' Mr Goodall said.

Wildo stood up and answered again. Mr Goodall ignored him and asked another question. Nobody answered. Mr Goodall pointed at me and called my name. I didn't know I knew the answer. I wanted to stand up slowly, to kill time. But I was there, standing. I gave an answer.

'That is correct,' Mr Goodall said.

80   I sat down. My forehead felt hot and sweaty, but I felt good. Then in schoolyard at recess time, Wildo joked about it. Listen to what he had to say: 'Delroy Brown isn't only a big head. Delroy Brown can answer questions with big mouth.'

'Yeh!' the gang roared, to tease me.

Then Wildo had to say, 'If only he could get a *mouth-organ*.' All the boys laughed and walked away.

I went home to lunch and as usual I came back quickly. Wildo and Jim and Desmond and Len were together, at the

90 bench, under the palm tree. I went up to them. They were swapping mouth-organs, trying out each one. Everybody made sounds on each mouth-organ, and said something. I begged Len, I begged Desmond, I begged Jim, to let me try out their mouth-organs. I only wanted a blow. They just carried on making silly sounds on each other's mouth-organs. I begged Wildo to lend me his. He didn't even look at me.

I faced Wildo. I said, 'Look. I can do something different as a Mouth-organ Boy. Will you let me do something

100 different?'

Boy, everybody was interested. Everybody looked at me.

'What different?' Wildo asked.

'I can play the comb,' I said.

'Oh yeh,' Wildo said slowly.

'Want to hear it?' I asked. 'My dad taught me how to play it.'

'Yeh,' Wildo said. 'Let's hear it.' And not one boy smiled or anything. They just waited.

110   I took out my comb. I put my piece of tissue paper over it. I began to blow a tune on my comb and had to stop. The boys were laughing too much. They laughed so much they staggered about. Other children came up and laughed too. It was all silly, laughing at me.

I became angry. Anybody would get mad. I told them they could keep their silly Mouth-organ Boys business. I told them it only happened because Desmond's granny gave him a mouth-organ for his birthday. And it only caught on because Wildo went and got a mouth-organ too. I didn't sit with the boys in class that afternoon. I didn't care what
120   the boys did.

I went home. I looked after my goats. Then I ate. I told my mum I was going for a walk. I went into the centre of town where I had a great surprise.

The boys were playing mouth-organs and dancing. They played and danced in the town square. Lots of kids followed the boys and danced around them.

It was great. All four boys had the name 'The Mouth-organ Boys' across their chests. It seemed they did the name themselves. They cut out big coloured letters for the words from newspapers and magazines. They gummed the letters down on a strip of brown paper, then they made a hole at each end of the paper. Next a string was pushed through the holes so they could tie the names round them. The boys looked great. What a super name: 'The Mouth-organ Boys'! How could they do it without me!

'Hey, boys!' I shouted, and waved. 'Hey, boys!' They saw me. They jumped up more with a bigger act, but ignored me. I couldn't believe Wildo, Jim, Desmond and Len enjoyed themselves so much and didn't care about me.

I was sad, but I didn't follow them. I hung about the garden railings, watching. Suddenly I didn't want to watch any more. I went home slowly. It made me sick how I didn't have a mouth-organ. I didn't want to eat. I didn't want the lemonade and bun my mum gave me. I went to bed.

Mum thought I wasn't well. She came to see me. I didn't want any fussing about. I shut my eyes quickly. She didn't want to disturb me. She left me alone. I opened my eyes again.

If I could drive a truck I could buy loads of mouth-organs. If I was a fisherman I could buy a hundred mouth-organs. If I was an aeroplane pilot I could buy truck-loads of mouth-organs. I was thinking all those things and didn't know when I fell asleep.

Next day at school the Mouth-organ Boys sat with me. I didn't know why but we just sat together and joked a little bit. I felt good running home to lunch in the usual bright sunlight.

I ran back to school. The Mouth-organ Boys were under the palm tree, on the bench. I was really happy. They were really unhappy and cross and this was very strange.

Wildo grabbed me and held me tight. 'You thief!' he said.

The other boys came around me. 'Let's search him,' they said.

'No, no!' I said. 'No.'

'I've lost my mouth-organ and you have stolen it,' Wildo said.

'No,' I said. 'No.'

'What's bulging in your pocket, then?'

170 'It's mine,' I told them. 'It's mine.'

The boys held me. They took the mouth-organ from my pocket.

'It's mine,' I said. But I saw myself up to Headmaster. I saw myself getting caned. I saw myself disgraced.

Wildo held up the mouth-organ. 'Isn't this red mouth-organ mine?'

'Of course it is,' the boys said.

'It's mine,' I said. 'I got it at lunchtime.'

'Just at the right time, eh?' Desmond said.

180 'Say you borrowed it,' Jim said.

'Say you were going to give it back,' Len said.

Oh I had to get a mouth-organ just when Wildo lost his!

'My mother gave it to me at lunchtime,' I said.

'Well, come and tell Teacher,' Wildo said.

Bell rang. We hurried to our class. My head was aching. My hands were sweating. My mother would have to come to school, and I hated that.

Wildo told our teacher I stole his mouth-organ. It was no good telling Teacher it was mine, but I did. Wildo said

190 his mouth-organ was exactly like that. And I didn't have a mouth-organ.

Mr Goodall went to his desk. And Mr Goodall brought back Wildo's grubby red mouth-organ. He said it was found on the floor.

How could Wildo compare his dirty red mouth-organ with my new, my beautiful, my shining clean mouth-organ? Mr Goodall made Wildo Harris say he was sorry.

Oh it was good. It was good to become one of 'The Mouth-organ Boys'.

Illustrated by Sean Victory

67

THE POW-WOW DRUM

Long black braids and silken shawls
Moving side by side where the eagle calls,
Answering the beat of the pow-wow drum
we come again
to dance again

Hey-a, Hey-a, Hey-a, Hey-a, Hey!
Hey-a, Hey-a, Hey-a, Hey-a, Hey!

Leave the dusty cities far behind,
Meet our brothers of the country with one mind,
Travelling from the east, north, south and west
we come again
to dance again

Hey-a, Hey-a, Hey-a, Hey-a, Hey!
Hey-a, Hey-a, Hey-a, Hey-a, Hey!

Watching close the feet of lightning fly
Fancy dancers free underneath the sky,
Joining in the circle moving round and round
we come again
to dance again

Hey-a, Hey-a, Hey-a, Hey-a, Hey!
Hey-a, Hey-a, Hey-a, Hey-a, Hey!

Women shining like the morning sun,
Children making rainbows as they laugh and run,
The old and young meeting like they did long ago
we come again
to dance again

Hey-a, Hey-a, Hey-a, Hey-a, Hey!
Hey-a, Hey-a, Hey-a, Hey-a, Hey!

DAVID CAMPBELL

Illustrated by
Emma Chichester Clarke

69

THE SNAKE SONG

Neither legs nor arms have I
But I crawl on my belly
And I have
Venom, venom, venom!

Neither horns nor hoofs have I
But I spit with my tongue
And I have
Venom, venom, venom!

Neither bows nor guns have I
But I flash fast with my tongue
And I have
Venom, venom, venom!

Neither radar nor missiles have I
But I stare with my eyes
And I have
Venom, venom, venom!

I master every movement
For I jump, run and swim
And I spit
Venom, venom, venom!

JOHN MBITI

Chicken Dinner

Mama, don' do it, please
Don' cook that chicken fe dinner,
We know that chicken from she hatch
She is the only one in the batch
That the mangoose didn't catch,
Please don' cook her fe dinner.

Mama, don' do it, please,
Don' cook that chicken fe dinner,
Yuh mean to tell me yuh feget
Yuh promise her to we as a pet?
She not even have a chance fe lay yet
And yuh want fe cook her fe dinner.

Mama, don' do it, please,
Don' cook that chicken fe dinner,
Don' give Henrietta the chop,
I tell yuh what, we could swop
We will get yuh one from the shop
If yuh promise not to cook her fe dinner.

Mama, me really glad yuh know
That yuh never cook Henny fe dinner,
And she really glad too, I bet,
Oh, Lawd, me suddenly feel upset.
Yuh don' suppose is somebody else pet
We eating now fe dinner?

VALERIE BLOOM

Illustrated by Derek Brazell

No Gun for Asmir

CHRISTOBEL MATTINGLY

Asmir comes from Bosnia Herzegovina. That name twists the tongues of people who do not know it. But Asmir was born in Sarajevo. And it rolls off his tongue like the smooth creamy sauce and the tender tasty meat of his grandmother's *musaka*.

Asmir remembers how the mountains rose sparkling with snow in the winter all around Sarajevo. And in the summer the trees swept like green waves up the slopes. The domed roofs of the mosques gleamed like moons among the houses and the minarets spiked the skyline. Morning, noon and evening the
10   *muezzins'* call to prayer used to echo out across the city.

Asmir's father, Muris, was a lawyer in Sarajevo. Asmir's mother, Mirsada, was a chemical engineer in a chocolate factory. Asmir's brother Eldar was still only a baby, just twelve months old.

But Asmir had many other playmates. They used to meet each day in the park near their homes, running among the trees, chasing, hiding, swinging, see-sawing, rolling on the grass, calling, laughing.

Until one day, war came to Sarajevo. Hundreds of
20   soldiers arrived, firing rifles, firing guns. Tanks rumbled through the street. Aircraft flew over the city dropping bombs.

The smell of burning made Asmir's stomach sick. The smoke made his eyes sting. The sight of his friend the postman lying on the street with all the letters spilling out of his bag made his heart shudder. It was too late to help the postman. Asmir gathered up the bloodstained letters. But when he took them to some of the addresses, the houses were burning heaps or hollow holes. He ran home clutching the crumpled envelopes. His grandmother washed his hands and cooked him *ustipci*. They were his very favourite. But that day he could not swallow. The pancakes stuck in his throat.

40 Morning and night the tanks rumbled and the rockets exploded. Midday the sky filled with droning planes and the crack of snipers' rifles. There was no electricity to amplify the *muezzins'* call. It seemed to Asmir as if the soldiers had bombed God.

Then they bombed the chocolate factory. The smell of the chocolate choked Asmir to the bottom of his lungs and made his stomach churn. The chocolate burned but his mother came home. Asmir hugged her tight, and that night he crept into bed between her and his father. And the bad
50 dreams went away.

Day after day, night after night, week after week the war went on. Grandmother came to live with them because her apartment was gone. Meat became a treat, eggs were as scarce as hens' teeth. Of course there was no chocolate. And no ice cream or lemonade either. Then there was no milk.

The daffodils were dancing in the park. The cherry trees were frothing white like the milk Asmir's father had loved on top of his coffee. But the playground had become a
60 bomb crater and a cemetery. Two of Asmir's friends had been killed there. Another was in hospital. He would walk again only if he was given an artificial leg.

'Mirsada, there are no medicines left in the hospitals and no pain-killing drugs. You must go somewhere safe with the children,' Muris said to Asmir's mother. 'It's time for you to leave while you can. They're still letting women and children go. But tonight could be the last time they do.'

Asmir saw his mother's face go pale and watched her dark eyes grow even darker. They looked like black holes of
70 emptiness. She gripped her husband's hands. 'But Eldar has a fever. Can't we go tomorrow when he is better?'

'It's still safer in Serbia. You must go to your sister Melita in Belgrade,' Muris said. Asmir loved his aunt Melita.

His father said to him, 'Pack your holiday rucksack with your favourite toys and some for Eldar too. And help your mother choose some clothes. You can't take everything.'

Asmir put in their teddies, his best Lego and a bag of little farm animals, Eldar's cart and horse on wheels, a boat for the bath, some books, his coloured pencils and drawing pad. His mother crammed T-shirts, jeans, shorts, pyjamas, shoes and socks into a case.

Eldar was so restless that his mother slept beside him that night. So Asmir slept with his father. It was good to snuggle up with him. 'Why do we have to go away?' he asked. 'I don't want to leave you. Can't you come with us?'

'I wish I could,' his father said. 'But the war is getting worse every day. Yugoslavia has broken up. Serbia wants to take over Bosnia. That's why their army has invaded us.'

Invade. It was a crushing word. Asmir felt pinned down by it. As his friend had been by the falling wall.

His father went on, 'And women and children must have first chance to escape.'

Escape. A scary, running word. Almost worse than invade. His friend whose leg had been torn off by shrapnel couldn't run. He couldn't even walk. He couldn't escape.

'Why do we have to escape? Who are we escaping from?' Asmir's voice came out as a whisper in the dark.

'We're Muslim, Asmir. And they want to clean us out.'

'But we're clean already,' Asmir said, thinking of the washing dancing on the line, the gleaming copper cooking pots his grandmother loved to scour, the shining tiled floor, the crisp fresh clothes he put on each day. He stroked the smooth soft sheet. It was as soft as his grandmother's cheeks. And nobody could be cleaner than she was. 'Why do they want to clean us out? They're going about it in a very messy stupid way.'

He thought of the shattered glass, the piles of rubble, the splintered doors and sagging beams of houses in their

74

110 own street, the proud trees in the playground blasted, split, stripped of their dancing leaves, dying.

'Who are they, anyway?'

His father groaned with a sigh that seemed to come from somewhere deeper than the graves Asmir had seen men digging in his park, even deeper than the bomb crater. 'Lots of them were our friends, Asmir. Some of them were our neighbours. Your mother and I went to school and university with some of them. Your grandmothers played with their parents.'

'Then why are they fighting? It doesn't make sense.'

'War never does make sense,' Asmir's father said sadly. Asmir
120 shivered and snuggled closer to him.

'Innocent people get hurt. Coming home from work one day your mother and I were caught between gunfire from both sides. We worry what would happen to you and Eldar if we were hurt.'

Asmir shuddered and tried to blot out the picture of the postman from his mind – so still, so crumpled. So bloody. 'Will they make you fight and kill people too?'
The words stuck in his throat. Like the pancakes had.

'They'll make some people. But I don't want to kill anyone,
130 Asmir. I'll volunteer to work in the hospital. They'll need every pair of hands they can get to care for the wounded.'

'I wish I could stay and help you,' Asmir said.

'You have a job to do too,' his father said. 'You'll have to look after your mother and Eldar and grandmother now.'

'When will we come back?'

'I don't know. I only wish I did.'

Asmir suddenly felt old. Old and heavy. And very tired. His father put his arms around him. And that was all that mattered now.
140 He fell asleep on his father's shoulder.

When he woke, the sunbeams were shimmering with dancing dust. Asmir coughed. There was always dust now from the bombing. He shivered. The bed was cold. He turned over. The bed was empty. 'Daddy,' he called. But there was no answer. Muris was gone.

Illustrated by Peter Sutton

75

Black Beauty

ANNA SEWELL

One day, whilst our cab and many others were waiting outside one of the Parks, where a band was playing, a shabby old cab drove up beside ours. The horse was an old worn-out chestnut, with an ill-kept coat, and bones that showed plainly through it. The knees knuckled over, and the forelegs were very unsteady. I had been eating some hay, and the wind rolled a little lock of it that way, and the poor creature put out her long thin neck and picked it up, and then turned round and looked about for more. There was a hopeless look in the dull eye that I could not help noticing, and then, as I was thinking where I had seen that horse before, she looked full at me and said, 'Black Beauty, is that you?'

It was Ginger! but how changed! The beautifully arched and glossy neck was now straight and lank, and fallen in, the clean straight legs and delicate fetlocks were swelled; the joints were grown out of shape with hard work; the face, that was once so full of spirit and life, was now full of suffering, and I could tell by the heaving of her sides, and her frequent cough, how bad her breath was.

Our drivers were standing together a little way off, so I sidled up to her a step or two, that we might have a little quiet talk. It was a sad tale she had to tell.

After a twelvemonth's run off at Earlshall, she was considered to be fit for work again, and was sold to a gentleman. For a little while she got on very well, but after a longer gallop than usual the old strain returned, and after being rested and doctored she was again sold. In this way she changed hands several times, but always getting lower down.

'And so at last,' said she, 'I was bought by a man who keeps a number of cabs and horses, and lets them out. You look well off, and I am glad of it, but I could not tell you what my life has been. When they found out my weakness, they said I was not worth what they gave for me, and that I must go into one of the low cabs, and just be used up; that is what they are doing, whipping and working with never one thought of what I suffer; they paid for me, and must get it out of me, they say. The man who hires me now pays a deal of money to the owner every day, and so he has to get it out of me too; and so it's all the week round and round, with never a Sunday rest.'

I said, 'You used to stand up for yourself if you were ill-used.'

'Ah!' she said, 'I did once, but it's no use; men are strongest, and if they are cruel and have no feeling, there is nothing that we can do, but just bear it, bear it on and on to the end. I wish the end was come. I wish I was dead. I have seen dead horses, and I am sure they do not suffer pain.

I wish I may drop down dead at my work, and not be sent off to the knacker's.'

I was very much troubled, and I put my nose up to hers, but I could say nothing to comfort her. I think she was pleased to see me, for she said, 'You are the only friend I ever had.'

Just then her driver came up, and with a tug at her mouth backed her out of the line and drove off, leaving me very sad indeed.

A short time after this a cart with a dead horse in it passed our cab-stand. The head hung out of the cart-tail, the lifeless tongue was slowly dropping with blood; and the sunken eyes! but I can't speak of them, the sight was too dreadful. It was a chestnut horse with a long thin neck. I saw a white streak down the forehead. I believe it was Ginger; I hoped it was, for then her troubles would be over. Oh! if men were more merciful, they would shoot us before we came to such misery.

Unwillingly to School

Distracted, the mother said to her boy,
'Do you try to upset and perplex and annoy?
Now, give me four reasons – and don't play the fool –
Why you shouldn't get up and get ready for school.'

Her son replied slowly, 'Well, Mother, you see,
I can't stand the teachers and they detest me;
And there isn't a boy or a girl in the place
That I like or, in turn, that delights in my face.'

'And I'll give you two reasons,' she said, 'why you ought
Get yourself off to school before you get caught;
Because, first, you are forty and, next you young fool,
It's your job to be there.
You're the head of the school.'

GREGORY HARRISON

Illustrated by Sholto Walker

Conversation Piece

Late again Blenkinsop?
What's the excuse this time?
Not my fault sir.
Whose fault is it then?
Grandma's sir.
Grandma's. What did she do?
She died sir.
Died?
She's seriously dead all right sir.
That makes four grandmothers this term.
And all on PE days Blenkinsop.
I know. It's very upsetting sir.
How many grandmothers have you got Blenkinsop?
Grandmothers sir? None sir.
None?
All dead sir.
And what about yesterday Blenkinsop?
What about yesterday sir?
You missed maths.
That was the dentist sir.
The dentist died?
No sir. My teeth sir.
You missed the test Blenkinsop.
I'd been looking forward to it too sir.
Right, line up for PE.
Can't sir.
No such word as can't. Why can't you?
No kit sir.
Where is it?
Home sir.
What's it doing at home?
Not ironed sir.
Couldn't you iron it?
Can't do it sir.
Why not?
My hand sir.
Who usually does it?
Grandma sir.
Why couldn't she do it?
Dead sir.

Illustrated by Sholto Walker

GARETH OWEN

Acknowledgements

Toothie and Cat by Gene Kemp, from *Dog Days and Cat Naps* by Gene Kemp
(Faber & Faber 1980). Reprinted by permission of Faber and Faber on behalf of the author
Licked by Paul Jennings, from *Unbearable!* by Paul Jennings (Penguin Books Australia 1990).
Reprinted by permission of Penguin Books Australia Ltd
Telling Tales by Trevor Harvey, © the author, Trevor Harvey (1998)
Abducted by Aliens by Ian Souter, © the author Ian Souter (1998)
My Mother Saw a Dancing Bear, What has Happened to Lulu? by Charles Causley,
both poems from *Figgie Hobbin* (Macmillan). Reprinted by permission of David Higham Associates
on behalf of the author
Friend or Foe by Michael Morpurgo from *Friend or Foe* by Michael Morpurgo
(William Heinemann, a division of Egmont Children's Books). Reprinted by permission of Egmont
Children's Books on behalf of the author, © Michael Morpurgo
Up in the Attic by Wes Magee, © the author Wes Magee (1995)
The Concrete Poem by Noel Petty, from *Does W Trouble You?*, edited by Gerard Benson
(Viking 1994). Reprinted by permission of the author, © Noel Petty 1994
The Platform Arriving ... by Gina Douthwaite, from *Picture a Poem* by Gina Douthwaite
(Hutchinson 1994). Reprinted by permission of Random House on behalf of the author,
© Gina Douthwaite 1994
In the Beginning and Pandora's Box by Geraldine McCaughrean. Taken and adapted from
The Orchard Book of Greek Myths by Geraldine McCaughrean, first published in the UK in 1992 by
Orchard Books, a division of the Watts Publishing Group, 96 Leonard Street, London EC2A 4RH
How Night Came to the World, The Fox and the Crane, The Tortoise and the Baboon
retold by Sean Taylor. Reproduced with permission of the Celia Catchpole Agency
on behalf of the author, © Sean Taylor (1998)
Bedd Gelert retold by Stephen Corrin, from *Stories for Nine Year Olds*
by Sarah and Stephen Corrin (Faber & Faber 1979)
Beth Gêlert by William Robert Spencer (out of copyright)
The Highwayman by Alfred Noyes, from *Collected Poems by Alfred Noyes* (John Murray).
Reprinted with permission of John Murray (Publishers) Ltd
A Smuggler's Song by Rudyard Kipling, reprinted with permission of A. P. Watt Ltd
on behalf of The National Trust
Beauty and the Beast retold by Dennis Hamley © Dennis Hamley (1998)
Billy Beast by Laurence Anholt, from Billy Beast, *a Seriously Silly Story*, first published in the UK
by Orchard Books, a division of the Watts Publishing Group, 96 Leonard Street, London EC2A 4 RH
Grandpa Chatterji by Jamila Gavin from *Grandpa Chatterji* by Jamila Gavin (Methuen).
Reprinted with permission of David Higham Associates on behalf of the author
The Mouth-organ Boys by James Berry, from *A Thief in the Village and Other Stories*
by James Berry (Hamish Hamilton 1987). Copyright © James Berry (1987)
The Pow-wow Drum by David Campbell, © 1994 David Campbell, from *A Caribbean Dozen*
edited by John Agard and Grace Nichols. Illustrated by Cathie Felstead.
Reproduced by permission of the publisher Walker Books Ltd, London
The Snake Song by John Mbiti from *Can I Buy a Slice of Sky*, edited by Grace Nichols
(Knight Books/Hodder and Stoughton 1991)
Chicken Dinner by Valerie Bloom, from *Duppy Jamboree* by Valerie Bloom (Cambridge University
Press 1992). Reproduced by permission of Cambridge University Press, © Valerie Bloom (1992)
No Gun for Asmir by Christobel Mattingly, from *No Gun For Asmir* by Christobel Mattingly
(Penguin Books Australia 1993)
Black Beauty by Anna Sewell (out of copyright)
Unwillingly to School by Gregory Harrison, first published in *A Fourth Book of Poetry* edited by
John Foster (OUP). By permission of the author, © Gregory Harrison
Conversation Piece by Gareth Owen, from *Salford Road* by Gareth Owen (HarperCollins).
Reprinted with permission of HarperCollins Publishers Ltd

*Every effort has been made to trace copyright holders
but we would be glad to rectify any omissions at the next reprint.*